4-2-64

THE
SOLUBILITY PRODUCT
PRINCIPLE

THE
SOLUBILITY PRODUCT
PRINCIPLE

AN INTRODUCTION TO ITS USES
AND LIMITATIONS

BY

S. LEWIN, M.Sc., Ph.D.

Head of the Science Department, South-West Essex Technical College

LONDON
SIR ISAAC PITMAN & SONS, LTD.

27891

First published 1960

SIR ISAAC PITMAN & SONS, Ltd.
PITMAN HOUSE, PARKER STREET, KINGSWAY, LONDON, W.C.2
THE PITMAN PRESS, BATH
PITMAN HOUSE, BOUVERIE STREET, CARLTON, MELBOURNE
22–25 BECKETT'S BUILDINGS, PRESIDENT STREET, JOHANNESBURG

ASSOCIATED COMPANIES
PITMAN MEDICAL PUBLISHING COMPANY, Ltd.
39 PARKER STREET, LONDON, W.C.2
PITMAN PUBLISHING CORPORATION
2 WEST 45TH STREET, NEW YORK
SIR ISAAC PITMAN & SONS (CANADA), Ltd.
(INCORPORATING THE COMMERCIAL TEXT BOOK COMPANY)
PITMAN HOUSE, 381–383 CHURCH STREET, TORONTO

MADE IN GREAT BRITAIN AT THE PITMAN PRESS, BATH
F0—(T.891)

To the Memory of my Father and my Mother

Preface

IN 1889 Nernst[1] formulated the *concentration* solubility product principle and described its quantitative application. The principle has been used qualitatively and quantitatively to explain the well-known common ion effect and the general precipitations and solubilizations in qualitative and quantitative inorganic analysis; but during the last thirty years the principle has been used more frequently as an *activity* solubility product. In common with many other mathematical expressions, the principle suffers from the disadvantage of decreasing degree of accuracy associated with increased range of application. Among the many limitations on the use of the solubility product principle are two outstanding ones which unfortunately received little attention.

The first limitation applies to the method of derivation of the solubility product principle. The present literature considers the equilibrium to be one between the solid phase and its *anhydrous* ions in solution and neglects to take into consideration any possible variations in the activities of both *solvent* molecules and the solid phase. As will be seen later, these activities are variable, at constant temperature and pressure, and the arbitrary assumption that they are constant in somewhat dilute solution is likely to result in error.

The second limitation is concerned with the attainment of equilibrium conditions. The solubility product treatment assumes that stable—thermodynamic—equilibrium conditions are present. However, most inorganic precipitations take place with great rapidity, i.e., under non-equilibrium conditions. Hence, theoretically, the correctness of the application of available solubility product data to the corresponding precipitations under non-stable conditions is open to question. Indeed, rapid precipitations are known to result not in the precipitation of the thermodynamically stable solid phases, but in the formation of non-stable states such as finely divided particles having greater solubility product values than the corresponding ones applying to crystals of ordinary size, the formation of metastable solid forms, the precipitation of greatly contaminated products and non-stable solid solutions, the production of highly hydrated solids or gels and other non-stable forms depending on the experimental conditions. This shows that the application of the

vii

solubility product value for the stable solid existing in stable—thermodynamic—equilibrium with its saturated solution, to conditions where rapid precipitations take place, is inaccurate. The fact that the application of available solubility product data to precipitations of the respective electrolytes in qualitative analysis does explain in many cases qualitatively the type of precipitation taking place is merely a fortunate series of coincidences which allow a high percentage error, as will be seen later. Indeed, there are many cases where the application of the available solubility product values do not result in correct prediction of precipitation—for example, the failure to precipitate nickel or zinc sulphides in acid solutions on addition of hydrogen sulphide.

The appreciation of chemistry as a scientific subject can suffer considerably if it be taught as a series of laws or unrelated generalizations and properties. For scientific education it is essential to teach chemical principles, their operative ranges, their limitations and possible correlations. What scientists seek in the scientific field is not just a series of laws, but the pattern and the background of these "laws." In the elementary stage of teaching chemistry it may be difficult to make the average student appreciate the significance of scientific patterns. However, in all subsequent stages it is essential—if one is not to produce a generation of uneducated chemists having the belief that chemistry is just a series of laws and regulations—to emphasize that chemical laws are merely approximations and that the limitations to these generalizations are as important as the laws themselves, if not more so.

The teaching of the various ranges of the applications and limitations of the solubility product principle lends itself particularly well to the above purpose because of the correlation between kinetic and thermodynamic aspects of stable equilibria, the possibilities associated with the lack of stable equilibrium conditions when precipitations take place, effects of dipole moments on solvation, and so on. This opportunity tends to be neglected in some teaching institutions in that, while qualitative analysis forms an important part of the *practical* curriculum at the intermediate stages, partly because of the plea that it can be used to illustrate the *theoretical* principles of many inorganic reactions, emphasis on the practical details is insisted upon to the partial, if not major, exclusion of the theoretical aspects. When any explanations are given, they are usually in terms of the *reduced* solubility product equations; the *comprehensive* solubility product equation is usually unheard of.

This book is an attempt to cover—in as simple a language as possible; and in general, but not in detail—the uses and limitations of the solubility product principle in ionic precipitations and solubilities. It is impossible to cover all, or even most of, the available facts in an introductory book of this size. But I hope that by approaching this principle on a new basis, collecting together the major aspects of the subject and raising and re-interpreting several others, this book will contribute towards a greater understanding of the uses and limitations of the solubility product principle.

It is hoped that this book will be equally useful to teachers and students whose work involves the use of the solubility product principle and to all others who apply the principle in chemical analysis.

I should like to thank Dr. L. Peters for reading and criticizing the final manuscript and proofs.

My thanks are also due to Dr. J. Jackson, Mr. A. W. Ellis, B.Sc., Mr. R. D. Langstaff, B.Sc., for proof corrections and to Mr. J. S. McCall, M.Sc., and the various postgraduate and undergraduate students who read and corrected errors in the manuscript.

Contents

Preface vii

Introduction xv

CHAPTER 1

DERIVATION OF THE SOLUBILITY PRODUCT PRINCIPLE . . 1

General—Derivation of *reduced* activity solubility product in terms of *anhydrous* ions—Derivation of the comprehensive activity solubility product—Limitations of the reduced solubility product principle—Limitations of the concentration solubility product

CHAPTER 2

SOLUBILITY PRODUCT AND SOLUBILITY 11

General—Common ion effect—Application to qualitative analysis— Precipitation and solution under equilibrium conditions—Fractional precipitation

CHAPTER 3

SOLID SOLUTIONS AND BASIC SALTS 16

Solid solutions—Basic salts

CHAPTER 4

CHANGE OF MEDIUM AND DEHYDRATION EFFECTS . . 22

The competition of co-soluble salts for water of hydration

CHAPTER 5

COMPLEX ION FORMATION 28

Formation of complex ions—Formation of ammines—Precipitation control in Qualitative Analysis

CHAPTER 6

THE SIGNIFICANCE OF THE SOLUBILITY PRODUCT IN RELATION TO PARTIAL IONIZATION 33

The effect of partial ionization on the application of solubility products to solubility—Aquo-metal acids—Suggested distinction between ionization and dissociation

Contents

CHAPTER 7

VARIATION OF EQUILIBRIUM CONSTANTS WITH TEMPERATURE 37

Equilibrium constants and heats of reaction—Endothermic and exothermic reactions—Water activity and its effect on some hydroxide precipitations

CHAPTER 8

LACK OF EQUILIBRIUM CONDITIONS 41

Theory and practice—Bancroft's Statement—Ostwald's Law of Successive Transformations—Experimental assessment of the precipitation ratio
(Ionic Product/Solubility Product)—Theoretical assessment of the precipitation ratio

CHAPTER 9

THE SIGNIFICANCE OF THE SOLUBILITY PRODUCT IN NON-STABLE
CONDITIONS 47

APPENDIX 1

THERMODYNAMIC DERIVATION OF THE COMPREHENSIVE SOLUBILITY
PRODUCT EQUATION 52

APPENDIX 2

SOLID ACTIVITY 54

APPENDIX 3

IONIC STRENGTH 59

APPENDIX 4

DIPOLE MOMENTS 62

APPENDIX 5

ACTIVITY AND ACTIVITY COEFFICIENTS 65

APPENDIX 6

CONSIDERATIONS RELATING TO THE APPLICABILITY OF THE
COMPREHENSIVE SOLUBILITY PRODUCT EQUATION . . . 70

APPENDIX 7

SOLUBILITY PRODUCT VALUES 76

Contents xiii

APPENDIX 8

THE TEACHING AND STUDY OF THE SOLUBILITY PRODUCT

PRINCIPLE 79

Examples and Problems 87

Bibliography 97

References. 100

Solutions to Problems 103

Author Index 115

Subject Index 116

Introduction

THE search for mathematical expressions to cover the solubility of electrolytes in the absence or presence of other electrolytes has proceeded for some time, and many equations have been advanced.* However, none has attained the degree of success which has been achieved by the application of the solubility product principle. In 1889, Nernst[1] formulated this principle as the classical, *concentration* solubility product and showed that the precipitations arising from addition of common ions could be accounted for by it, in several cases. The attempts to apply this product over the entire field of electrolyte solubility had, however, to contend with the difficulty of assessment of the degree of partial ionization of the various electrolytes involved. Such an assessment was complicated by complex ion formation and by the assumption, then prevalent, that the so-called strong electrolytes were partially ionized. At the outset of the experimental work it might have been argued that, if the results were to be in disagreement with the concentration solubility product principle, the principle was nevertheless correct and that any disagreement was due to incorrect interpretation of the conductivity data which resulted in incorrect percentages of ionization being calculated. The difficulty involved in the interpretation of the experimental results can be illustrated by Noyes'[4] work. This investigator used mixtures containing common ions such as $AgBrO_3$ and $AgNO_3$, $TlNO_3$ and KNO_3, and other salts. Now, while the mixtures of silver salts gave results which agreed with the principle, the mixtures of thallium salts gave contrary results. Noyes[5] showed,

* For example, the Bancroft School[2] attempted to explain the solubilities of various salts in terms of equations such as

$$(X + A)y^n = C; \text{ or } (X + A)(Y + B)^n = C$$

where X and Y represent the weights of solvent and solute respectively, and A B, n and C are empirical constants.

The equation

$$\log \left(\frac{v}{\dfrac{1}{v} + \dfrac{1}{N_2}} \right)^v = -\frac{L_f}{4 \cdot 58} \left(\frac{1}{T} - \frac{1}{T_m} \right)$$

has been suggested by Hildebrand[3] where L_f = molar heat of fusion, v = number of ions in the electrolyte, N_2 is the mole fraction of the solute, T_m = the melting point of the pure solid, and T is the experimental temperature in degrees absolute.

xv

however, that assuming the correctness of the concentration solubility product, the results in the case of $TlNO_3$ and KNO_3 could be used to calculate the degree of ionization, in agreement with Ostwald's Law of Dilution. However, such an approach need not result in the correct interpretation being reached. Indeed, Kendall[6] interpreted his own results—for mixtures of slightly soluble organic acids—as showing that the evaluation of the degree of ionization from solubility data by the application of the concentration solubility product principle is open to question. Naturally, such an interpretation cast doubt on the general validity of the principle. Results obtained by other investigators also showed lack of agreement with the principle. Thus,[7] the addition of lanthanum nitrate to lanthanum iodate resulted in the solubility of the latter first decreasing, but then increasing. It was also found that in some cases, assuming the principle to hold, the solubilities of the respective salts were such that they were smaller than the corresponding concentration of the undissociated salt (which the theory assumed to be constant). But even apart from the quantitative difficulties experienced, the application of the *concentration* solubility product principle failed completely to explain the increase in solubility obtained on addition of "neutral" salts (i.e. those not containing a common ion). Stieglitz[8] attacked even the theoretical derivation of the solubility product principle. He pointed out that the Law of Mass Action does not apply to strong electrolytes and went as far as saying that the concentration "solubility product principle . . . is an approximate empirical principle which is without theoretical foundation."

The position at the end of the first score of years of the twentieth century may be summed up by the statement that the concentration solubility product, though qualitatively correct in many cases, was in quantitative agreement with experiment only in very dilute solutions, such as $10^{-5}N$, and even in this region some discrepancies have been found in certain instances.

The problem of correlating those cases which followed the concentration principle with many of those that did not was, however, resolved as the concept of activity became generally accepted. As activities were substituted for concentrations, quantitative agreement between the experimental results and the activity, or thermodynamic, solubility product was attained. Indeed, the reverse process was now being applied, that is, assuming the correctness of the new principle, the solubility results were used to calculate the activity coefficient values. Thus, Brønsted and LaMer[9] interpreted their experimental results as demonstrating the correctness of the Debye-Hückel[10] theory in calculating activity coefficient values. Brønsted,[11] using the activity coefficient concept and his Principle of Specific Interaction of Ions, was able to explain the effects of neutral salts on the solubility of sparingly soluble salts.

The activity solubility product replaced the concentration solubility product. The fact that activity coefficients were partly empirical in origin and value—certainly over ionic strength values above 0·1—was neglected. The activity solubility product—formulated on the impossible assumption that anhydrous ions were being dealt with in solution—was considered firmly established. Any deviations from the activity product could be considered apparent and due to some "specific ionic effects" and additional—but nevertheless *empirical*—constants or parameters. Further, many other problems and questions, such as those noted in the preface to this book, were considered only in passing, or simply ignored.

CHAPTER 1

Derivation of the
Solubility Product Principle

THE derivation of the solubility product principle can be carried out from either kinetics or thermodynamics. Both will be considered in turn, but it should be noted that the common treatment in the literature, kinetic or thermodynamic, uses only the equilibrium

solid ⇌ anhydrous ions

in solution, and this type of derivation will be considered first. Since electrolytes owe their solubility in water almost solely to the association of their ions with water molecules, it is difficult to see how the equilibrium involving only anhydrous ions can be considered correct. Consequently, we shall expound later a new derivation and use of the solubility product principle in terms of an equilibrium involving association of ions with water molecules.

Derivation of the Reduced Activity Solubility Product in Terms of Anhydrous Ions

Consider a solid M_xA_y in equilibrium with its saturated solution, at constant temperature and external pressure. Let the equilibrium be represented as one between the solid and its anhydrous ions (and possible intermediate un-ionized molecules), thus

$$\overset{\text{I}}{M_xA_y} \rightleftharpoons \overset{\text{II}}{M_xA_y^*} \rightleftharpoons xM^{z+} + yA^{z-} \qquad . \quad . \text{ (A)}$$

$$\underset{\text{solid}}{} \qquad \underset{\text{saturated solution}}{}$$

*M_xA_y in solution may be considered either a covalent unit or as an association of ions behaving as a single entity. Whether this unit exists or not is immaterial to the derivation of the solubility product principle; but it does enter into the relation between the solubility product and the solubility.

1

Assuming that the Law of Mass Action applies to the heterogeneous equilibrium (because the homogeneous equilibrium in solution is associated with, or is dependent on, the constant vapour pressure of the solid), we have

$$\frac{(a_{M_xA_y})_{solution}}{(a_{solid})} = K_I \qquad \qquad (1)$$

and

$$\frac{(a_+)^x(a_-)^y}{(a_{M_xA_y})_{solution}} = K_{II} \qquad \qquad (2)$$

where (a_+) and (a_-) represent the activities of the respective ions and K_I and K_{II} are the equilibrium constants of the respective equilibria. Rearranging (1) and substituting the value for $(a_{M_xA_y})_{solution}$ into (2), we obtain

$$\frac{(a_+)^x(a_-)^y}{K_I(a_{solid})} = K_{II} \qquad \qquad (3)$$

It follows that

$$(a_+)^x(a_-)^y = K_I K_{II}(a_{solid}) \qquad \qquad (4)$$

If we assign to the activity of the solid a constant value or unity we obtain

$$(a_+)^x(a_-)^y = K_s \qquad \qquad (5)$$

where K_s is a constant known as the ionic activity, or thermodynamic, solubility product. For convenience we shall refer to this constant as the *reduced* activity solubility product, to distinguish it from the *comprehensive* activity solubility product which will be developed later.

In very dilute solutions, such as 10^{-5}N, the activity of an ion is practically equal to its concentration, and in such ranges we may substitute concentrations for activities. The above equation then reduces to

$$[M_+]^x[A_-]^y = K_c \qquad \qquad (6)$$

Nernst's classic concentration solubility product principle may thus be derived for *very dilute* solutions.

Thermodynamically there are several ways of deriving the activity solubility product in terms of the equilibrium involving anhydrous ions with solid. We shall consider only one of these in terms of equilibrium (A), p. 1.

The chemical potential of a given species distributed between two phases at equilibrium is the same in both phases, and consequently

$$\mu_{\text{solid}} = \mu_{\text{undissociated}} = x\mu_+ + y\mu_- \qquad . \qquad . \qquad (7)*$$

where μ represents the chemical potential and the suffices refer to the respective entities.

It follows that at thermodynamic equilibrium

$$(a_+)^x(a_-)^y = \text{a constant} \qquad . \qquad . \qquad . \qquad (8)$$

the value of this constant is obviously the same as that in equation (5). As before, when one deals with very dilute solutions, such as about 10^{-5}N, concentrations may be substituted for activities, thus giving rise to equation (6).

Derivation of the Comprehensive Activity Solubility Product

A saturated aqueous solution in equilibrium with the solid form of the solute involves the reversible reaction

$$\text{Solid} + \text{water} \rightleftharpoons \text{Saturated solution}$$

Taking a solid electrolyte M_xA_y, we have for the above, at constant temperature and external pressure

$$\underset{\text{solid}}{M_xA_y} + \underset{\text{solvent}}{(xb + yc)H_2O} \rightleftharpoons \underset{\text{hydrated ions in solution}}{x(M^{z^+} \cdot bH_2O) + y(A^{z^-} \cdot cH_2O)} \qquad (B)$$

where z^+ and z^- are the respective charges of the cation and the anion, and b and c are the respective numbers of water molecules associated with the ions. The Law of Mass Action applies strictly only to a homogeneous equilibrium and not to a heterogeneous equilibrium such as the one above. However, we can overcome this difficulty by assuming that we are dealing with two coexistent equilibria—

(1)
$$\underset{\text{solid}}{M_xA_y} \rightleftharpoons \underset{\text{vapour}}{M_xA_y} \qquad . \qquad . \qquad . \qquad (C)$$

and

(2)
$$\underset{\text{vapour}}{M_xA_y} + \underset{\text{solvent}}{(xb + yc)H_2O} \rightleftharpoons \underset{\text{saturated solution}}{x(M^{z^+} \cdot bH_2O) + y(A^{z^-} \cdot cH_2O)} \qquad (D)$$

in which the second equilibrium is associated with or is dependent on the first equilibrium. Now, the vapour pressure

* See Appendix I.

represents the activity of the solid with respect to the second, homogeneous, equilibrium. Consequently, when stable equilibrium conditions exist, we have by the Law of Mass Action

$$\frac{(a_+)^x(a_-)^y}{(a_{\text{solid}})(a_{\text{H}_2\text{O}})^{(xb+yc)}} = K \qquad . \qquad . \qquad . \qquad (9)$$

which is the *comprehensive* activity solubility product equation (see Lewin[12]).

Thermodynamically, the same result can be achieved by the use of chemical potentials (see Appendix 1).

Rewriting the last equation, we have

$$(a_+)^x(a_-)^y = K(a_{\text{solid}})(a_{\text{H}_2\text{O}})^{(xb+yc)} \qquad . \qquad . \qquad (10)$$

Now if, and only if, one deals with solutions sufficiently dilute then (a_{solid}) and $(a_{\text{H}_2\text{O}})^{(xb+yc)}$ may alter only slightly, thus allowing approximation to the *reduced* activity, or concentration, solubility products.

Limitations of the Constancy of the Reduced Solubility Product

The reduced activity solubility product has been used extensively without any corrections for solid and solvent activities' variations by many investigators and authors for calculations of precipitations of chemical analysis where high concentrations of electrolytes were present. However, the activity of the solid, or its "vapour pressure" does vary with increasing concentration of the solution (see Appendix 2 where several considerations have been advanced to illustrate this effect). Further, the activity of the water itself alters with increase in concentration of the solution. Consider the polarity of water which is mainly responsible for the aqueous solubility of electrolytes. The dipolar arrangement of the water molecules may be represented as

$$\overset{\delta^-}{O}\overset{\overset{\displaystyle \overset{\delta^+}{H}}{\diagup}}{\underset{\underset{\displaystyle \underset{\delta^+}{H}}{\diagdown}}{}}$$

The ions of the electrolyte are associated with the water molecules, the negative end of the water dipole being oriented towards the positively charged ion, and the positive end of the dipole being directed towards the negatively charged ion. Thus, in the case of sodium chloride, one kind of association may be represented by

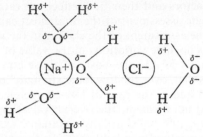

though, of course, several other combinations may exist, based on the same directional influences.*

Increasing ionic concentrations result in increased induced polarization along the associated dipole and this results in an overall increase in the dipole moment of the solvent. This alters the activity of the solvent which is largely dependent on the overall value of the dipole moment. The increase in the value of the dipole moment of the water results in two effects—

(i) Increased tendency for association of water molecules. This means an increase in the value of n in the empirical formula of water, $(H_2O)_n$, thus decreasing effectively the number of water units available, per given quantity of water, for association with the ions of the electrolyte. The result is a decrease in the value of a_{H_2O}.†

(ii) Increased tendency for association between the now more polar water units with the oppositely charged ions of the electrolyte, i.e. an increased a_{H_2O} value, so far as the water-ion interaction is concerned.‡

* It should be remembered that the diagram presented above gives only a two-dimensional picture. The correct representation is, of course, three-dimensional.

† The association between water molecules to form larger units may be pictured in terms of association between opposite dipoles of different water molecules which is assisted by the tendency to form hydrogen bonds (. . . . .), thus

$$H\overset{\delta+}{\rule{1.2cm}{0.4pt}}\overset{\delta-}{O}\text{--------}\overset{\delta+}{H}\rule{1.2cm}{0.4pt}\overset{\delta-}{O}\text{--------}\overset{\delta+}{H}\rule{1.2cm}{0.4pt}\overset{\delta-}{O}_{\delta-}$$

It has been estimated that the value of n may be as high as 6. In practice there is a dynamic equilibrium between $(H_2O), (H_2O)_2 . . . . . (H_2O)_6$. Increased dipole value tends to increase the overall value of n. Rise in temperature, owing to increase in thermal motion, tends to decrease the value of n.

‡ This is so because the greater the value of the dipole moment of the solvent the smaller is the electrical field between the oppositely charged ions of the electrolyte. (The effect is comparable to that of a condenser having two oppositely charged plates with a dielectric material between them. The greater the value of the dielectric constant the weaker is the field.)

6 *The Solubility Product Principle*

In equation (10), it is the combined effect of the above two factors on the value of $(a_{H_2O})^{(xb+yc)}$ which matters. Calculations of the values of these factors and their final effect are rather complicated, but an approximate assessment of the final effect can be made. This assessment and the assessment of the change in the variation in solid activity as well as possible variations in the value of K itself are considered in Appendix 5. On the basis of those considerations, it is possible to assess that, over the low ionic strength* of approximately $I = 0$ to $I = 0.01$ and in the case of low-charge electrolytes such as uni-univalent and uni-divalent, the overall variation in the value of the product $a_{solid}(a_{H_2O})^{(xb+yc)}$ is usually less than 2 to 3 per cent, while the value of any variation in K is likely to be less. Consequently the error involved in assuming the validity of the reduced solubility product equation instead of the comprehensive one in the above-mentioned cases and range is unlikely to exceed such small percentages. But with further ionic strength increase, and with increase in valency value, the value of the factor $a_{solid}(a_{H_2O})^{(xb+yc)}$ varies much more than originally and consequently the assumption that the reduced activity solubility product principle still applies, results in increasingly greater percentage errors. It is possible to miss, unwittingly, these factors when empirically determined constants and parameters are used. However, in view of the above analysis, the correctness of the use of such empirical quantities is questionable.

Limitations of the Concentration Solubility Product

The term activity may be replaced by the product (concentration × activity coefficient).† When the concentrations of the electrolyte are stated in molarities, i.e. in moles per litre, we have in terms of equation (5) which applies in very low ionic strengths—

$$\{[M^{z+}]f_{M^{z+}}\}^x\{[A^{z-}]f_{A^{z-}}\}^y = K_s \qquad . \qquad . \quad (11a)$$

or

$$(C_+f_+)^x(C_-f_-)^y = K_s \qquad . \qquad . \qquad . \quad (11b)$$

where the square brackets signify molarities and the "f" factors represent the corresponding molar activity coefficients; the use of C_+ and C_- for the corresponding molarities is employed in (11b).

Equation (11b) can be rewritten as

$$(C_+)^x(C_-)^y = \frac{K_s}{(f_+)^x(f_-)^y} \qquad . \qquad . \qquad . \quad (12a)$$

$$= \frac{K_s}{(f_\pm)^y} \qquad . \qquad . \qquad . \quad (12b)$$

* See Appendix 3.

† For variation in the values of the activity coefficients with concentration see Appendix 5.

Let $(C_+)^x(C_-)^y = K_c$ the classical concentration solubility product then

$$K_c = \frac{K_s}{(f_\pm)^y} \qquad . \qquad . \qquad . \qquad . \qquad (13a)$$

Similarly, it can be shown that when molalities are employed,

$$K_m = \frac{K_s}{(\gamma_\pm)^y} \qquad . \qquad . \qquad . \qquad . \qquad (13b)$$

where K_m is the classical solubility product expressed in molalities and $\gamma_\pm$ is the *molal* activity coefficient.

It follows from the above that the classical concentration solubility products have the same value as the activity solubility products only if the mean activity coefficients are unity. This is the case when infinitely dilute solutions are employed. However, the assumption involving equality is only approximately correct when we deal with very dilute solutions such as 10^{-4}N of the (slightly soluble) electrolyte. It is essential to emphasize that the activity coefficient of an ion is dependent on the *concentration of all the electrolytes in the solution, i.e. on the total number of ions present, and their charges, irrespective of their parentage.* In other words, the introduction of any foreign electrolyte into the solution already containing another electrolyte results in the activity coefficient of the latter being altered. Lack of appreciation of the importance of this point has resulted in the publication of several calculations involving a high degree of inaccuracy as they assumed K_c to be equal to K_s in presence of other electrolytes. Consider equation (13a). Three possibilities exist—

(a) $f_\pm = 1$ here $K_c = K_s$
(b) $f_\pm < 1$ here $K_c > K_s$
(c) $f_\pm > 1$ here $K_c < K_s$

Now, K_c is directly related to the solubility, i.e. increase in the value of K_c results in increase of solubility, while its decrease results in the solubility being decreased. It is clear therefore that the presence of foreign ionic species (those not having a common ion) can, by affecting K_c, greatly increase or decrease the solubility of a given electrolyte. As an illustration of the above consider the classical case of the solubility of AgCl.[13] Its solubility is increased in the presence of salts not having a common ion, while the presence of salts having a common ion results in the solubility of AgCl not following the line calculated on the basis of $K_c = K_s$, but rather following the curve utilizing the activity coefficient of AgCl.

Similar results have been obtained with other sparingly soluble substances such as barium sulphate[14] and calcium oxalate.[15] See Fig. 1.

From the above arguments it is to be expected that when $f_{\pm} > 1$ the previous effect will be reversed; that is, the solubility of the slightly soluble substance will be below that obtained in the absence of foreign electrolytes. However, this effect cannot be demonstrated because the value of $f_{\pm}$ becomes greater than unity only

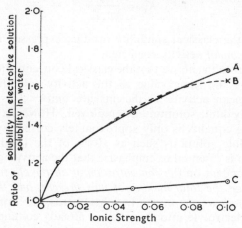

FIG. 1. RELATIVE INCREASE IN SOLUBILITY WITH INCREASE IN IONIC STRENGTH

   A. Relative increase in solubility of $BaSO_4$ in presence of KNO_3 (according to Neumann's results[14]).

   B. Relative increase in solubility of calcium oxalate monohydrate in NaCl solutions at 37°C (according to Hammarsten[15]).

   C. Relative increase in solubility of AgCl in presence of KNO_3 (according to Popoff and Neumann[13]).

above the range of ionic strengths where equation (5) and equation (11) apply. In these higher ionic strength ranges the comprehensive solubility product equation applies, and then

$$K_c = \frac{K(a_{\text{solid}})(a_{H_2O})^{(xb+yc)}}{(f_{\pm})^y} \qquad . \qquad . \qquad . \qquad (14)$$

Returning now to the question of what percentage error may be involved in the assumption that $K_c = K_s$ over the region of low ionic strengths, this is given by the equation (deducible from 13a).

$$\left(\frac{K_c - K_s}{K_s}\right) = \left(\frac{1}{(f_{\pm})^y} - 1\right) \qquad . \qquad . \qquad . \qquad (15)$$

Since $f_{\pm}$ varies with the total electrolyte concentration, the percentage accuracy will also be affected by such changes. Hence we require to know the variation of $f_\pm$ with ionic strength for the above assessment.

The activity coefficient values of some single species of electrolyte solutions are given in Appendix 4. The effect of the introduction of other electrolytes on the activity coefficient values of a specified electrolyte has not been determined in many cases, because of the obviously large number of possibilities involved. However, Lewis

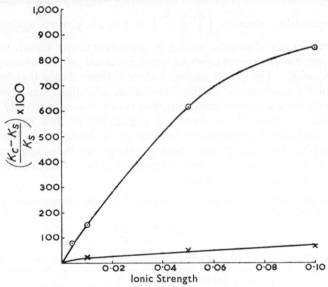

Fig. 2. Variation of the Percentage Error, involved in the Assumption that $K_c = K_s$, with Ionic Strength

— ⊙ — Bi-bivalent electrolyte.
— × — Uni-univalent electrolyte.

and Randall[16] pointed out that in very dilute solutions the activity coefficient value of a given strong electrolyte is the same in all solutions having the same ionic strength. When therefore the mean activity coefficient of a given electrolyte is known, it is reasonable to assume that it will be approximately the same in any solution of the same ionic strength, no matter what other electrolytes are present, provided we are dealing with low ionic strengths. Using this generalization and the Debye-Hückel relations for the mean activity coefficient values which are respectively over the approximate ionic strength range $I = 0$ to $I = 0.01$,

$$\log f_\pm = -Az^+z^- \sqrt{I} \qquad . \qquad . \qquad . \qquad (16)$$

and over the ionic strength range up to $I = 0.1$, for aqueous solutions, at 25°C*,

$$\log f_{\pm} = \frac{-Az^+z^- \sqrt{I}}{1 + \sqrt{I}} \qquad . \qquad . \qquad . \quad (17)$$

where A is a temperature-dependent constant, and z^+ and z^- are the respective charges on the ions, the mean activity coefficient values of uni-univalent and bi-bivalent electrolytes were calculated[17] and the corresponding values of $\left(\dfrac{K_c - K_s}{K_s}\right) \times 100$ are plotted against the respective ionic strengths, giving in accordance with equation (15) the approximate percentages of error involved in the assumption that $K_c = K_s$. The curves in Fig. 2 show without doubt that neglect of activity coefficients in the calculation of solubilities, even in relatively very low concentrations, can result in comparatively large percentage errors. It is therefore regrettable to find that many books and articles containing chemical calculations, while mentioning activity coefficients and even pointing out their importance, neglect to include an assessment of the effect in the actual calculations, it being assumed to be "small."

* The Debye-Hückel equation for the approximate ionic strength range of up to $I = 0.1$ may be written as

$$\log f_{\pm} = \frac{-Az^+z^- \sqrt{I}}{1 + Ba_i \sqrt{I}}$$

where B is a constant the value of which depends on the temperature and solvent, and a_i represents the mean distance of closest approach of the ions in the solution. For water at 25°C, this equation reduces to equation (17).

CHAPTER 2

Solubility Product and Solubility

THE relationship between the concentration solubility product and the solubility of an electrolyte which is completely dissociated in solution is comparatively simple. Consider, for example, a solid bivalent metal salt in equilibrium with its saturated solutions, thus,

$$\underset{\text{solid}}{MA_2} \overset{+(b+2c)H_2O}{\rightleftharpoons} \underset{\text{solution}}{(M^{++}bH_2O) + 2(A^-\cdot cH_2O)}$$

If the salt is sparingly soluble (e.g. about 10^{-5}M) and no other electrolytes are present, the activity coefficient values may be reasonably assumed to be practically equal to unity and the concentration solubility product applies.

Accordingly, equation (6) gives

$$[M^{++}][A^-]^2 = K_c$$

Let $[M^{++}] = x$, then $[A^-] = 2x$, and

$$x \times (2x)^2 = K_c$$

$$\therefore \quad x = \left(\frac{K_c}{4}\right)^{\frac{1}{3}}$$

= solubility of the metal ion in moles per litre.

Parallel equations can be developed for other cases. If, however, the sparingly soluble salt is more soluble than 10^{-5}M, say up to $I = 10^{-4}$, then for accurate calculations the reduced activity solubility product should be used, applying the Debye-Hückel equation to the calculation of the respective activity coefficients. Above $I = 10^{-4}$, there are some deviations in the numerical values of the activity coefficients from those calculated by the Debye-Hückel equations, in the case of 2:2 and higher valency electrolytes. The percentage

11

errors involved in the arbitrary application of the theoretical activity coefficient values in the calculations involving 1:1 electrolytes are comparatively small, i.e. of the order of 10 per cent up to $I = 0.1$. Over the same range, judging by some available data, 2:2 and higher valency electrolytes will give considerably larger differences, of the order of several score per cent. These considerations limit therefore the application of the *reduced activity* solubility product to very low ionic strengths when a high degree of accuracy is required. However, the qualitative uses of the principle over the wider ranges of solubility should not be decried. The limitation of the use of the solubility product principle is merely an example of the general rule, which applies to most generalizations and approximations, namely that the larger the range of application, the smaller the degree of accuracy.

Common Ion Effect

The addition of comparatively small quantities of salts, having a common ion, to a solution of a sparingly soluble salt in equilibrium with the solid results in the well-known common ion effect in which the solubility of the electrolyte is depressed, ultimately leading to precipitation. Thus, suppose that we have a saturated solution of a sparingly soluble salt, such as AgCl, in equilibrium with its solid, then since the activity solubility product value is 10^{-10}, that is, $(a_{Ag^+})(a_{Cl^-}) = 10^{-10}$, the activities can be replaced by concentrations and $[Ag^+][Cl^-] = 10^{-10}$.

Let $[Ag^+] = x$, then $[Cl^-] = x$ also (because when only AgCl is present, $[Ag^+] = [Cl^-]$)

$\therefore x^2 = 10^{-10}$, whence $x = 10^{-5}$

If we now add a small quantity of a chloride, then temporarily the new chloride ion concentration, say $[Cl^-]_2$ will exceed the value of the previous chloride ion concentration, and therefore, temporarily,

$$[Ag^+]_1[Cl^-]_2 > 10^{-10}$$

but this is not a stable equilibrium. For stable equilibrium the ionic product of the silver and chloride ions must be equal to 10^{-10}. Consequently, a rearrangement will take place until the new ionic product equals the value of the solubility product, namely, 10^{-10}. The precipitation of AgCl, which reduces both the silver ion and chloride ion concentrations, leads to the fulfilment of this requirement, thus resulting in a new, lower silver chloride concentration.

Such common ion effects can be calculated, comparatively accurately, on the basis of the reduced concentration solubility product equation, only for very small common ion additions. For higher total concentrations up to $I = 0.1$ the limitations previously pointed out apply.

Application to Qualitative Analysis

The solubility product principle has been extensively applied to explain the various precipitations and solubilities encountered in qualitative analysis. It should be pointed out at the outset that the solubility product principle, whether in the form of the comprehensive or reduced equations, applies only to stable equilibrium conditions, but the sudden precipitations and solubilizations encountered in qualitative analysis can by no means be considered to take place under anything approaching stable equilibrium conditions. Hence, such application is essentially arbitrary. The fact that various happenings in qualitative analysis *can* be qualitatively covered by the solubility product principle could be considered fortuitous and is primarily due to possible tremendous percentage errors of magnitudes of 10^5 to 10^7 per cent because of the enormous excess of ionic concentrations present above those required by the respective solubility product values.

The magnitude of such possible errors is so large that it completely swamps many other variations such as those due to neglect of activity coefficients of the solute, activity of the solid, activity of the water and the number of associated water molecules, as well as some complex ion formations and any significant changes of medium.

The limitations, associated with the lack of equilibrium conditions when precipitation takes place, and some possible consequences, will be considered in the section dealing with non-stable conditions.

Precipitation and Solution under Equilibrium Conditions

Consider the utilization of the solubility product principle under stable equilibrium conditions. The general applicable relationship is given by equation (10), namely

$$(a_+)^x (a_-)^y = K(a_{\text{solid}})(a_{\text{H}_2\text{O}})^{(xb+yc)}$$

which requires, of course, the presence of the appropriate stable solid. The question as to whether precipitation of extra solid, or solution of solid already present, will take place can be answered on the basis of the above equation by saying that for equilibrium, namely the *status quo*, to be maintained, the value of the left-hand side, i.e. the ionic product, must equal the value of the right-hand side, whereas for precipitation the ionic product must be greater than the value of the right-hand side, i.e.

$$(a_+)^x(a_-)^y > K(a_{solid})(a_{H_2O})^{(xb+yc)}$$

and for the solid to dissolve, the ionic product must be smaller than the value of the right-hand side, i.e.

$$(a_+)^x(a_-)^y < K(a_{solid})(a_{H_2O})^{(xb+yc)}$$

When very dilute solutions are employed, such as those below $I = 0·01$, it is possible to write—

Ionic Product = Solubility Product   for equilibrium
Ionic Product > Solubility Product   for precipitation
Ionic Product < Solubility Product   for solid to dissolve

and the lower the ionic strength and ionic charge, the more accurate the prediction.

Fractional Precipitation

The solubility principle can be applied to the assessment of fractional precipitation with certain reservations. Consider, for example, a solution containing electrolytes having two cations each of which can form a sparingly soluble salt with an anion not yet added, or a solution containing electrolytes having two anions each of which can form a sparingly soluble salt with an absent cation. The addition of an electrolyte containing the requisite anion or cation respectively to one of the above solutions results in precipitation. Qualitatively, the less soluble salt should be first precipitated followed by precipitation of the more soluble electrolyte. The question naturally arises: How effective may such a selective separation be? The question can be answered by application of the appropriate reduced activity solubility product equations to very dilute solutions. Consider, for example, a solution containing NaCl and NaI to which $AgNO_3$ is being added progressively. We have for the reduced solubility products

$$(a_{Ag^+})(a_{Cl^-}) \simeq 10^{-10}, \text{ and } (a_{Ag^+})(a_{I^-}) \simeq 10^{-16}$$

Hence,

$$[Ag^+][Cl^-](f_\pm)^2_{AgCl} \simeq 10^{-10}, \text{ and } [Ag^+][I^-](f_\pm)^2_{AgI} \simeq 10^{-16}$$

Now, in very dilute solutions, as Lewis and Randall[16] have pointed out, the activity coefficients of different ions have the same value (particularly when uni-univalent electrolytes are employed). Hence, at any fixed ionic strength—below about $I = 0.01$

$$(f_\pm)_{AgCl} \simeq (f_\pm)_{AgI}$$

Consequently,

$$\frac{10^{-10}}{[Ag^+][Cl^-]} \simeq \frac{10^{-16}}{(Ag^+)(I^-)}$$

and therefore

$$\frac{[Ag^+][Cl^-]}{[Ag^+][I^-]} \simeq \frac{10^{-10}}{10^{-16}} = 10^6$$

Now, this relation applies at any given, fixed ionic strength. The removal of the halides by precipitation does not, however, alter the ionic strength, since halide removal is compensated by an equivalent replacement by the nitrate ion. Hence, the ionic strength remains fixed and the above relationship applies at any specified $AgNO_3$ addition, where, of course, the $[Ag^+]$ in the numerator and denominator must be equal and consequently we are left with the condition

$$\frac{[Cl^-]}{[I^-]} \simeq 10^6, \text{ or } [Cl^-] \simeq 10^6[I^-]$$

i.e. the precipitation of the iodide, which before $AgNO_3$ addition was, say, equal to the chloride concentration, should proceed until the above condition is fulfilled. Only when the above ratio is exceeded, will the precipitation of AgCl begin.

The above treatment is correct provided very dilute solutions are employed and provided that no solid solution is formed between the resultant precipitated solids. However, there are many cases where solid solutions are formed—for example, AgCl and AgBr, and in such cases the above treatment is no longer applicable. This is so because the values of (a_{solid}) can no longer be assumed to remain constant at low ionic strengths as interaction takes place between the two solids. It is then essential to take into consideration in the overall assessment, the separate activities of the solid solution with respect to either equilibrium.

CHAPTER 3

Solid Solutions and Basic Salts

IN certain cases, precipitation from solution gives rise to solids the compositions of which do not agree with those of 'pure' compounds, but are rather intermediate between the compositions of known compounds. The two outstanding categories of such precipitations are solid solutions and basic salts. For the sake of convenience we shall consider the formation of these categories separately.

Solid Solutions

Just as there are stable solids in stable equilibrium with their surrounding media, and non-stable solids in non-stable equilibrium with their surroundings, so there are stable solid solutions in stable equilibrium with their surrounding media as well as non-stable solid solutions in non-stable equilibrium with their surroundings. The discussion of non-stable equilibria will take place in the section on non-stable conditions. Here we shall concern ourselves solely with stable solid solutions under stable equilibrium conditions. Examples are to be found in solids of mixed crystal formation, such as the alums, in stable equilibrium with their saturated solutions. The stability of such systems can be checked as no alteration whatsoever takes place in the physico-chemical properties or chemical composition on standing for quite some time. That this mixed crystal formation depends on the concentration of the respective ions in solution has been shown by several investigators who pointed out that under analytical conditions the primary precipitate obtained is not stable. However, on standing for some time equilibrium is obtained. This pattern of behaviour is general in the various cases studied. Consider, for example, the titration of a mixture of chloride and bromide ions in solution (for example, NaCl and NaBr) with silver nitrate. Since the solubility product of AgBr is lower than that

16

of AgCl, then (if the relation of the two solubility product values were the sole criterion) as $AgNO_3$ is being added, the precipitate obtained before the quantity of silver nitrate added becomes equivalent to the bromide should, at equilibrium, be silver bromide only. In practice a mixed chloride-bromide solid is formed, under such conditions, and its composition changes until equilibrium is reached. But even at equilibrium it consists of a mixed crystal of AgCl and AgBr and the following relation is obeyed—

$$\frac{[Br^-_{solution}][Cl^-_{precipitate}]}{[Br^-_{precipitate}][Cl^-_{solution}]} = D$$

where D is a constant which has been usually referred to as the distribution coefficient.[18] Strictly speaking one could refer to such a distribution coefficient as the solubility product of the solid solution in equilibrium with its aqueous saturated solution.

One's first reaction to this phenomenon is to attempt to assess whether the above "distribution coefficient" is a ratio of the respective concentration solubility products of AgBr and AgCl. On multiplying both numerator and denominator of the left-hand side of the above relation by $[Ag^+_{solution}]$, we obtain

$$\frac{[Ag^+_{solution}][Br^-_{solution}] \times [Cl^-_{ppt}]}{[Ag^+_{solution}][Cl^-_{solution}] \times [Br^-_{ppt}]} = \frac{K_{c(AgBr)}[Cl^-_{ppt}]}{K_{c(AgCl)}[Br^-_{ppt}]} = D$$

Now, D has been found experimentally to be constant, consequently, the left-hand side of the above equation should be constant too. Now, while the ratio of the two concentration solubility products is constant, the ratio $\frac{[Cl^-_{ppt}]}{[Br^-_{ppt}]}$ varies along the titration curve. Consequently, the left-hand side cannot be constant. This is indeed a paradox. However, this can be resolved readily if one applies the comprehensive solubility product to the above (solid solution) $\rightleftharpoons$ (saturated liquid solution) equilibrium. Thus

AgBr
AgCl
$\overset{+(b+c)H_2O}{\underset{+(\bar{b}+c')H_2O}{\rightleftarrows}}$
$\overset{Ag^+}{(bH_2O)}$ + $\overset{Br^-}{(cH_2O)}$

Solid
Solution
$\overset{Ag^+}{(bH_2O)}$ + $\overset{Cl^-}{(c'H_2O)}$

We obtain

$$\frac{(a_{Ag^+})(a_{Cl^-})}{(a_{\text{solid } Cl^-})(a_{H_2O})^{(b+c')}} = K_{(AgCl)s.s.}$$

and

$$\frac{(a_{Ag^+})(a_{Br^-})}{(a_{\text{solid } Br^-})(a_{H_2O})^{(b+c)}} = K_{(AgBr)s.s.}$$

where a_{Ag^+} a_{Cl^-}, and a_{Br^-} are the activities of the corresponding hydrated ions in solution, and $(a_{\text{solid } Br^-})$ and $(a_{\text{solid } Cl^-})$ represent the activities of the same solid solution towards the corresponding equilibria. The corresponding K values represent the comprehensive solubility products with respect to the solid solution. These are not likely to have the same values as the respective solubility products of the pure solids.

The above may be rewritten in terms of (a_{Ag^+}), thus

$$(a_{Ag^+}) = \frac{K_{(AgCl)s.s.}(a_{\text{solid } Cl^-})(a_{H_2O})^{(b+c')}}{(a_{Cl^-})}$$

$$= \frac{K_{(AgBr)s.s.}(a_{\text{solid } Br^-})(a_{H_2O})^{(b+c)}}{(a_{Br^-})}$$

Now, in halide precipitation titrations, such as those discussed here, the precipitated halide ion is replaced by the nitrate ion. Hence, assuming any dilution taking place during the titration to be practically negligible, the overall ionic strength remains practically the same. Consequently, (a_{H_2O}) may be assumed constant and rearranging the above, we obtain

$$\frac{K_{(AgBr)s.s.}}{K_{(AgCl)s.s.}} = \frac{(a_{\text{solid } Cl^-})(a_{Br^-})(a_{H_2O})^{(c'-c)}}{(a_{\text{solid } Br^-})(a_{Cl^-})}$$

Rewriting the above in terms of concentrations and activity coefficients, we have

$$\frac{K_{(AgBr)s.s.}}{K_{(AgCl)s.s.}(a_{H_2O})^{(c'-c)}} = \frac{[\text{solid } Cl^-](f_{\text{solid } Cl^-})[Br^-](f_{Br^-})}{[\text{solid } Br^-](f_{\text{solid } Br^-})[Cl^-](f_{Cl^-})}$$

Since the ionic strength remains practically constant,

$$(f_{Br^-}) = (f_{Cl^-})$$

Further, so far as the solid part is concerned, the ionic lattice constitution alters little when a chloride ion is substituted for a bromide and vice versa, hence the overall ionic field inside the solid phase alters but little; consequently the activity coefficients of the ions in the solid lattice should remain practically constant, at any rate over the major part of the titration curve, and therefore

$$\frac{K_{\text{(AgBr)s.s.}}}{K_{\text{(AgCl)s.s.}}.(a_{H_2O})^{(c'-c)}} = \frac{[\text{solid } Cl^-][Br^-]}{[\text{solid } Br^-][Cl^-]}$$

Now, since the ionic strength in solution remains constant the number of water molecules associated with the bromide ion and the chloride ion, namely c and c', should remain constant. Consequently, the value of the left-hand side must be constant, too. Thus, the experimental distribution coefficient expression can be derived theoretically. Similar treatment can be applied to other solid solution formations where common anions or common cations are involved.

Basic Salts

The term "basic salts" has been applied to precipitates obtained on addition of alkalis to metal salts which have been shown to contain the anion of the original salt as well as the metal ion and the hydroxide radical. (As such they may be considered perhaps in the class of solid solutions.) However, while some solid solutions contain water, e.g., the alums, others do not; and many of the basic salts in equilibrium with their solutions undoubtedly contain water. This and the associated basicity has contributed towards basic salts being considered and treated as a separate subject.

This term has been extended to cover other salts such as bismuth oxychloride by defining[19] basic salts as "salts in which the proportion of base to acid is greater than in normal salts." The composition of the freshly precipitated basic salt depends on the speed of precipitation and varies with time, but it eventually becomes constant, thus showing that—while the primary precipitate was non-stable—the final, aged precipitate is stable. It is significant that the final stable equilibrium composition is not necessarily a stoichiometric one and that it also depends upon pH. The problem naturally arises whether a solubility product equation can be applied to the equilibrium of such salts with their saturated solutions. Understanding of such applications and their limitations is easier if one approaches the existence of basic salts from the standpoint advocated here, namely that basic salts are hydrated solid electrolytes capable of having a variable space lattice in which the proportion of water is not necessarily fixed, and in which the proportion of different anions is also variable within the limits of electrical neutrality of the solid.

Having been accustomed to the concept that chemical compounds are stoichiometric,* many might consider the above concept of basic salts and that of the usual stoichiometric compound to be mutually exclusive or contradictory. However, this is by no means the case. When we are dealing with ordinary chemical compounds in the solid state, with definite and limited crystal lattices, in absence of any surrounding solutions, then free energy considerations show that only certain lattices possess minimum free energy contents. These minimal free energy configurations are the most likely to exist, because the sole free energy criteria in such cases are those associated with lattice free energy values. But, when such solids are placed in contact with solutions of certain compositions, the previous criteria are no longer the sole ones; there is now the further requirement that the algebraic sum of the various chemical potentials involved be equal to zero. What was originally a minimum potential on its own is no longer so.

The variation in the free energy content leading to equilibrium may take place in the following ways—

(*a*) The composition of the solid may change in that the proportion of the various ionic concentrations is altered. Thus, in the case of basic zinc sulphate the ratio of the sulphate ion concentration to that of the hydroxide ion concentration will vary, though the total number of negative charges will remain constant to allow for electrical neutrality.

(*b*) Physical association or chemical combination with water may take place—that is, the formation of stable bulky precipitates associated with water, such as stable gels or gelatinous precipitates. Such behaviour has been observed by the author in the titration curves of several salts—for example, zinc sulphate with sodium hydroxide, where at various positions along the curve—when stable equilibrium has been reached—the association of the "precipitate" with water varies considerably.

The two variations may take place simultaneously to minimize unfavourable lattice dimensions. Such variations in water content cannot, however, be noticed by the usual dry weight analytical methods, particularly because some of the water may be bound very weakly.

The above may appear rather a generalized picture. But more specific pictures can be given in terms of changes between the inner shell of co-ordinated water molecules and external ions, thus making possible a variety of co-ordinate complexes having different solid activities. Thus, in the case of basic zinc chloride, the following overall picture may be presented as shown in Fig. 3.

Here K_1 is the equilibrium constant for the substitution of one of the external Cl^- into the inner water shell of (1) giving rise to (2)

* In agreement with the Law of Constant Proportions.

and vice versa. K_2 represents the acid dissociation constant of the aquo-acid (2). K_3 represents the acid dissociation constant of the aquo-acid (1), and K_4 represents the acid dissociation constant of the aquo-acid (3) with the consequence that an anhydrous form of

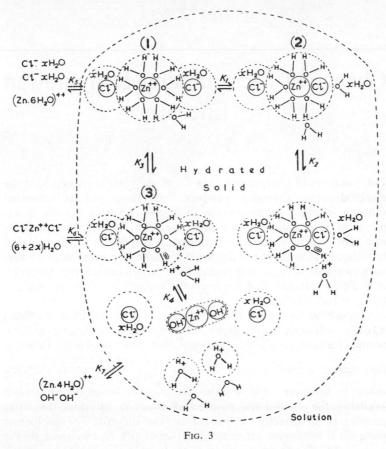

FIG. 3

zinc hydroxide is produced. K_5, K_6 and K_7 represent some possible equilibria between the respective forms of the solid and the corresponding forms in solution. Several other equilibria are also possible.

A complicated equation in terms of the comprehensive solubility product principle can be obtained on treatment of such equilibria, in the same way as has been done in connexion with solid solutions, but such development is outside the scope of this book.

CHAPTER 4

Change of Medium and Dehydration Effects

THE solubility of a substance varies with the solvent chosen, and the thermodynamic solubility product determined for its saturated solution in one solvent cannot, of course, be used for the determination of its solubility in another solvent. Ideally, the solubility of a substance in a mixture of solvents will follow a proportionality law, though in many cases this will be masked by some other factors such as association, or compound formation, between the molecules of the two solvents, and between the molecules of the solute and those of the solvent.

Suppose we have a saturated solution of a solute (P) in a solvent (Q), the solubility being dependent on some association or compound formation. The significance of the solubility value is that there is a fixed minimum ratio of $\dfrac{\text{moles of solvent}}{\text{mole of solute}}$ to keep the solute in solution. The smaller the number of moles of solvent available, the smaller the number of moles in solution, the latter number being directly dependent on the quantity of the former present. If we have a saturated solution of (P), and by some means we succeed in removing some of the solvent molecules—and each of the solvent molecules present in such a saturated solution is associated with the solute—then some of the molecules of the solute will be precipitated; and the quantity precipitated will be related directly to the number of molecules of solvent removed.

Consider again the saturated solution of (P) in a given quantity of solvent (Q) and assume again that it dissolves because of some association or compound formation between itself and the solvent molecules (Q). Then the addition of another solvent, or substance,

22

(S)—in which (P) is insoluble—which is ideally miscible with (Q), should not result in the precipitation of (P) since the total quantity of (Q) has not altered. However, if some association between the two solvents takes place, some of the (Q) molecules which form part of the minimum quantity necessary to keep the given quantity of (P) in solution will be removed in association with (S). Since the solution was originally saturated with (P), some of the latter molecules will be precipitated.

A similar treatment can be applied to the precipitation of NaCl from its saturated aqueous solution on the introduction of HCl.

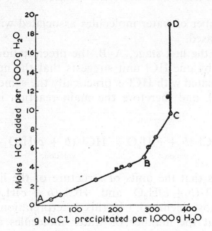

FIG. 4. PRECIPITATION OF NaCl FROM ITS SATURATED SOLUTION ON HCl
ADDITION

This process has been attributed by Mellor,[94] Partington[77] and others to the common ion effect associated with the solubility product. However, this explanation does not cover the facts, because the introduction of HBr or HI to an aqueous saturated solution of NaCl also causes the precipitation of the latter. Similarly, the addition of KOH to a saturated solution of NaCl causes the precipitation of the latter. In neither case is any common ion effect possible.

Let us analyse the experimental results of Ingham[95] for the solubility of NaCl in HCl solution and recalculate them on the basis of g NaCl precipitated per 1,000 g of water in a saturated solution on addition of various quantities of HCl. On plotting these recalculated results we obtain Fig. 4.

It follows from the graph that the ratio $\dfrac{\text{moles NaCl precipitated}}{\text{mole HCl added}}$

remains remarkably constant, and practically equal to unity, over the range A to B, i.e. up to 5 molal HCl. The constant value obtained for the precipitation of NaCl over the range C to D indicates that we are dealing there with a medium essentially hydrochloric acid in character—in which NaCl has a constant solubility—and not with an essentially aqueous medium. The range B to C indicates a transition from the essentially aqueous medium of A to B to the essentially hydrochloric acid medium of C to D. The main reaction in the latter range is therefore

$$HCl \cdot (b + c)H_2O + xHCl \rightleftharpoons (x + 1)HCl \cdot (b + c)H_2O \qquad (E)$$

that is, the number of water molecules associated with a single unit of HCl is decreased.

Returning to the first stage, A–B, the precipitation of practically one NaCl unit by one HCl unit suggests that the number of water molecules associated with HCl is practically the same as that associated with NaCl, and therefore the main reaction in this range is essentially

$$HCl + \overset{+}{Na}\overset{-}{Cl} \cdot (b + c)H_2O \rightleftharpoons \overset{+}{H}\overset{-}{Cl} \cdot (b + c)H_2O + NaCl \qquad (F)$$

gas   solution   solution   solid

It also indicates that the units of structure of the liquid phase are those of $NaCl \cdot (b + c)H_2O$ and $HCl \cdot (b + c)H_2O$, which are apparently almost identical. If this interpretation is correct we should find that the number of water molecules associated with NaCl or HCl in their respective solutions are identical. It is therefore illuminating to note that the number of water molecules associated with NaCl in its saturated solution is about 8·5, while that associated with HCl in its constant boiling mixture under atmospheric pressure —about 5N HCl—is approximately 8, thus indicating that under competitive conditions one H^+Cl^- unit is likely to displace one Na^+Cl^- unit. Further confirmation can be obtained from density measurements; since if the unit structures of the liquid phase are almost identical up to about 5N HCl—in the NaCl-HCl mixtures— and then a change takes place, we should expect a linear lowering of density (as the heavier Na^+ is replaced by the lighter H^+) up to about 5N HCl, and then a break in the density curve, thus indicating a changed state in the liquid structure. Indeed, a very pronounced break in the density curve has been noted by Ingham between 4·5N HCl and 5·5N HCl in the NaCl-HCl mixtures.

The above general thesis of precipitation-solubility equivalence, involving a competitive struggle for water molecules, may be considered in terms of a simplified mathematical treatment[20] for a system involving the solvent water and only two solutes, A and B.

Let P_A and P_B represent the minimum numbers of moles of water required per mole of A and of B to remain in solution; let S_A and S_B represent the numbers of moles of A and B existing in a co-saturated solution, and W_A and W_B represent the numbers of water moles associated with S_A and S_B, respectively. Then

$$W_A = S_A P_A \qquad \text{(ia)}$$

and

$$W_B = S_B P_B \qquad \text{(ib)}$$

Let the total quantity of water, in which S_A and S_B have dissolved in the co-saturated state be W, then

$$W = W_A + W_B \qquad \text{(ii)}$$

$$= S_A P_A + S_B P_B \qquad \text{(iii)}$$

Consider any two, different, co-saturated solubility data (marked by ′ and ″) for A and B for a fixed number of moles of water, W. Then,

$$S'_A - S''_A = \frac{W'_A}{P_A} - \frac{W''_A}{P_A} = \frac{W'_A - W''_A}{P_A} \qquad \text{(iv)}$$

and

$$S''_B - S'_B = \frac{W''_B}{P_B} - \frac{W'_B}{P_B} = \frac{W''_B - W'_B}{P_B} \qquad \text{(v)}$$

Therefore

$$\frac{S'_A - S''_A}{S''_B - S'_B} = \frac{W'_A - W''_A}{W''_B - W'_B} \times \frac{P_B}{P_A} \qquad \text{(vi)}$$

But

$$W = W'_A + W'_B$$

$$= W''_A + W''_B \qquad \text{(vii)}$$

Rewriting the last equation we have

$$W'_A - W''_A = W''_B - W'_B$$

Hence,

$$\frac{W'_A - W''_A}{W''_B - W'_B} = 1 \qquad \text{(viii)}$$

Substituting this result into equation (vi), we obtain

$$\frac{S'_A - S''_A}{S''_B - S'_B} = \frac{P_B}{P_A} \qquad \text{(ix)}$$

The Solubility Product Principle

The left-hand side of equation (ix) represents the difference between the numbers of moles of A existing in solution between the two co-saturated states ' and co-saturated states ", as the number of moles of B was altered from S'_B to S''_B. Hence, the above left-hand-side ratio can be expressed in terms of moles of A precipitated per mole of B added to the solution. Since P_A and P_B are constants, the above ratio is constant and if the saturation co-solubility data are plotted in the form of moles of A precipitated against moles of B added, the plot should be a straight line and its slope should be equal to the

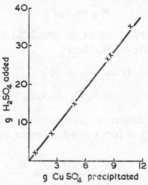

FIG. 5. PRECIPITATION OF $CuSO_4$ FROM ITS SATURATED SOLUTION (PER 100 g H_2O) ON ADDITION OF H_2SO_4 (AT 0°C)
The plot is based on recalculation of the data of Engel.[91]
The original data are given also in Seidell's *Solubilities of Inorganic and Metal Organic Compounds*, 3rd. ed. p. 503, D. Van Nostrand Co. Inc., New York, 1940.

above minimum water requirements ratio. It should, however, be clear that the value of P of any substance is likely to alter with considerable change in its solvent medium, such as takes place when the concentration of the co-solute is very high. Hence, the straight line relationship is likely to hold over initial ranges only. Further, the ratio P_B/P_A represents the ratio of *minimum* water requirements and should not be confused with the hydration numbers determined experimentally in *dilute* solutions, where there does not exist any competition for the water molecules. Hence, comparison of the above ratio with corresponding hydration number ratios may not lead to any useful conclusions, particularly since different methods result in different values for the hydration number of a given substance.

To test the above straight line conclusions, the experimental results of several investigators, for various co-saturated cases, were recalculated and replotted in the form of moles (or grammes) of A precipitated on introduction of moles (or grammes) of B. The above straight line conclusions were found to apply in the various cases examined. To illustrate the effect the plots of the recalculated values are given for the cases of $CuSO_4/H_2SO_4$, NaOH/NaCl and KOH/ KCl; see Figs. 5, 6 and 7, respectively. Other cases have been considered by the author elsewhere.[20]

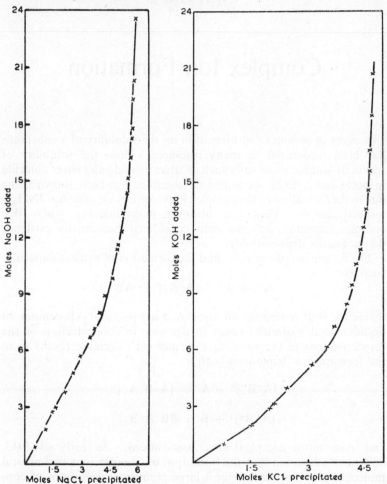

FIG. 6. PRECIPITATION OF NaCl FROM ITS SATURATED SOLUTIONS ON ADDITION OF NaOH (AT 25°C)

The plot is based on recalculations of Akerlof and Short's data.[92] See also Seidell, p. 1232.

FIG. 7. PRECIPITATION OF KCl FROM ITS SATURATED SOLUTIONS ON ADDITION OF KOH (AT 25°C)

The plot is based on recalculations of Akerlof and Short's data.[92] See also Seidell, p. 759.

CHAPTER 5

Complex Ion Formation

THE effect of complex ion formation on the solubility of a substance has been recognized in many instances. Thus, the solubility of sparingly soluble silver salts such as silver cyanide and silver chloride in potassium cyanide or ammonia solutions has been shown to be due to the formation of the complex ions $[Ag(CN)_2]^-$ and $[Ag \cdot 2NH_3]^+$ respectively.[21,22] There are, however, many instances where this complex formation has not been considered because its existence was not easily demonstrable.

The formation of ion pairs and the formation of neutral molecules such as

$$A^+ + B^- \rightleftharpoons [A^+B^-]^0 \rightleftharpoons AB$$

where $[A^+B^-]^0$ represents an associated ion pair and AB denotes an undissociated molecule) result in decrease in concentration of the respective ions in the solution. Further such decrease results from the formation of triple ions such as

$$[A^+B^-]^0 + A^+ \rightleftharpoons [A^+B^-A^+]^+$$

$$[A^+B^-]^0 + B^- \rightleftharpoons [B^-A^+B^-]^-$$

and even more complex ionic associations. As early as 1913, Schanov[23] suggested that the formation of complex ions and neutral molecules was responsible for a large number of deviations of conductivity measurements from Ostwald's Law of Dilution. Later, Bjerrum[24] formulated à mathematical theory accounting for the effect of Coulombic forces on complex ion formation, and Fuoss[25,26], and Fuoss and Kraus[27,28,29], extended the theory further and showed its applicability to a number of cases.

The phenomenon of complex ion formation is therefore of general occurrence and does indeed tend to increase with increase in concentration of the respective ions. Let us consider in this connexion the solubility of cadmium sulphide in concentrated HCl solutions. This has been attributed to the small sulphide ion concentration due to the suppression of dissociation of H_2S in acid solutions. But it has been pointed out by Belcher[30] and by others that experimental observations on the solubility of cadmium sulphide in strong HCl solutions do not agree with the values calculated on the basis of the concentration solubility product of cadmium sulphide. There is no doubt that in acid solutions suppression of the dissociation of H_2S does take place, thus decreasing the sulphide ion concentration and therefore decreasing the chances of the ionic product being greater than the solubility product value. There is also no doubt that the activity coefficients of cadmium and sulphide ions play a considerable part in this deviation. However, one must not neglect the following possible equilibria (or their equivalents[31,32,33])—

$$[Cd \cdot 4H_2O]^{++} + Cl^- \rightleftharpoons [\overset{++}{Cd} \cdot 3H_2O \cdot Cl^-]^+ + H_2O$$

$$[Cd \cdot 4H_2O]^{++} + 2Cl^- \rightleftharpoons [\overset{++}{Cd} \cdot 2H_2O \cdot 2Cl^-]^0 + 2H_2O$$

$$[Cd \cdot 4H_2O]^{++} + 3Cl^- \rightleftharpoons [\overset{++}{Cd} \cdot H_2O \cdot 3Cl^-]^- + 3H_2O$$

$$[Cd \cdot 4H_2O]^{++} + 4Cl^- \rightleftharpoons [\overset{++}{Cd} \cdot 4Cl^-]^= + 4H_2O$$

It has been noted by the author[17] that some such combination affects the precipitation of cadmium sulphide from chloride solutions. A series of solutions containing 0·1M $CdCl_2$ and increasing concentrations of NaCl, up to 4M, was made in distilled water. On bubbling H_2S through the various solutions it was found that the greater the amount of NaCl present, the smaller was the quantity of cadmium sulphide precipitated. Further, when the cadmium chloride was made up in a saturated solution of lithium chloride (about 10M), the bubbling of H_2S did not result in the formation of cadmium sulphide precipitate. Instead only a faint yellow colour was observed, possibly due to the formation of some colloidal cadmium sulphide. If now some distilled water be added on to the top of the solution, immediate precipitation of some CdS is noted in the mixed layers. These experiments and parallel experiments show that in sufficiently concentrated chloride ion solutions, the complex formation between the cadmium ions and the chloride ions is sufficiently great to stop cadmium sulphide precipitation on bubbling H_2S into neutral solutions where ordinarily it is readily precipitated.

Complex ion formation need not, of course, take place between ions only, as association of ions and non-ions is possible. Consider, for example, the effect of the addition of ammonia and ammonium chloride in Group III of the Qualitative Tables. Many text books consider that the addition of ammonium chloride is effective by virtue of the common ion—namely the NH_4^+ ion—effect in suppressing the dissociation of NH_4OH, and thus decreasing the OH^- concentration to an extent which is sufficient to cause precipitation of the ferric hydroxide, chromium hydroxide and aluminium hydroxide in Group III, but insufficient to exceed the solubility product values of the metal hydroxides of Mg, Ni, Co, Zn and Ca. It can be calculated roughly—particularly so because of the considerations relating to the lack of stable equilibrium conditions during the precipitation—that this may be the main factor in the lack of precipitation of $Mg(OH)_2$. But much higher concentrations than the maximum possible concentration of NH_4Cl—about 5N—would be required for the common ion effect of decrease in the OH^- concentration to be effective. The author has pointed out[17] that the non-precipitation of cobalt, nickel and zinc hydroxides in Group III can be interpreted in terms of the following formulations involving a rather simplified picture of the result of ammonia addition in terms of OH^- favouring precipitation and NH_3 complex formation favouring solubility. Thus

$$Ni \cdot xNH_3^{++} \underset{\text{solution}}{\overset{K_1}{\rightleftharpoons}} xNH_3 + Ni^{++}$$
$$+$$
$$2OH^-$$
$$\Big\Updownarrow K_2$$
$$\underset{\text{solid}}{Ni(OH)_2}$$

Therefore

$$[Ni^{++}] = K_2/[OH^-]^2$$

$$[Ni \cdot xNH_3]^{++} = [Ni^{++}][NH_3]^x/K_1$$

Consequently, the total quantity of nickel in solution is

$$[Ni^{++}] + [Ni^{++} \cdot xNH_3] = \frac{K_2}{[OH^-]^2} + \frac{K_2[NH_3]^x}{[OH^-]^2K_1}$$

$$= \frac{K_2}{[OH^-]^2}\left\{1 + \frac{[NH_3]^x}{K_1}\right\}$$

As the ammonia concentration rises, the factor of unity becomes increasingly negligible in comparison with the second factor in the brackets, and the total nickel concentration is given by

$$[Ni^{++}] + [Ni^{++} \cdot xNH_3] = \frac{K_2}{K_1} \left(\frac{[NH_3]^x}{[OH^-]^2} \right)$$

Thus, the solubility of nickel is proportional to

$$\frac{[NH_3]^x}{[OH^-]^2}$$

where the value of x increases up to six with rise in ammonia concentration. It is evident therefore that increase in ammonia concentration should progressively favour increase in nickel solubility. This interpretation can be easily verified by addition of a small quantity of ammonia to a nickel salt when the nickel hydroxide is first precipitated. Further addition of ammonia results in the nickel redissolving. One can reverse this effect by adding sodium hydroxide, when the nickel hydroxide is reprecipitated, because the formation of the nickelate ion in alkaline solutions is very small.

It is in this light that the function of the addition of ammonium chloride to Group III precipitation should be considered and a further assessment of this effect is possible. We may write the overall equilibria present in ammonia solution for qualitative purposes as

$$NH_3 + H_2O \rightleftharpoons NH_4OH; \qquad K_3 = [NH_4OH]/\{[NH_3][H_2O]\}$$

$$NH_4OH \rightleftharpoons NH_4^+ + OH^-; \qquad K_4 = [NH_4^+][OH^-]/[NH_4OH]$$

Rewriting these equilibria in terms of the constants involved, we have

$$[NH_4OH] = [NH_3][H_2O]K_3$$

$$= [NH_4^+][OH^-]/K_4$$

Hence,

$$\frac{[NH_3]}{[OH^-]} = \frac{[NH_4^+]}{K_4 K_3 [H_2O]}$$

Assuming $[H_2O]$, K_3 and K_4 to be constant, the value of the right-hand side increases with increase in ammonium ion, or of the ammonium chloride, concentration, and simultaneously the value of the ratio $[NH_3]/[OH^-]$ increases, too. This result is, however, only approximate, because activity coefficients have been neglected; the value of $[H_2O]$

4—(T.891)

decreases with increase in ammonium chloride concentration—and thus increases the above assessed effect—as it represents the amount of water available for interaction, but at higher salt concentrations (owing to association with the ions) it is bound to be smaller than the usual value of about 55·5 (assuming the molecular weight to be 18). Further, complexing of the metal ion with the chloride ion, introduced on addition of ammonium chloride, is bound to play a part of some significance.

CHAPTER 6

The Significance of the Solubility Product in Relation to Partial Ionization

THE solubility product principle may be derived irrespective of whether ionization is complete or partial. Many sparingly soluble electrolytes are only partially ionized in solution, and since the relation between solubility product and solubility depends on the degree of ionization, it might be thought that applicability of the solubility product concept in such cases is far less significant than in completely ionized electrolytes. This is not so. Rather it is the reverse in that correlation of the solubility product value—as determined by electrometric methods which assess ionic activities—with solubility results, assessed by analytical methods such as gravimetric or volumetric, can be used to calculate the degree of ionization in solution.

Consider a sparingly soluble bivalent metal hydroxide—whose saturation solubility is, say, 10^{-5} molal, and whose activity coefficient values can therefore be reasonably assumed practically equal to unity—which is partially ionized thus

$$\underbrace{M(OH)_2}_{\text{solid}} \rightleftharpoons \underbrace{M(OH)_2}_{\text{saturated}} \rightleftharpoons \underbrace{M^{++} + 2OH^-}_{\text{solution}}$$

The electrometric determination of the concentration solubility product, K_c—see equation (6), p. 2—gives $K_c = [M^{++}][OH^-]^2$. Analytical methods, such as volumetric or gravimetric, give the total concentration of the metal hydroxide in solution, i.e. the sum of the concentrations of the ionized and un-ionized forms. If the presence of the un-ionized fraction is ignored and the total concentration (H)

33

of the metal hydroxide is put equal to the concentration of the metal ions $[M^{++}]$, then the hydroxyl ion concentration is $2H$, and the solubility product determined by the latter method is $K_H = 4H^3$. Let the ionized fraction in solution be α, then $[M^{++}] = \alpha H$ and $[OH^-] = 2\alpha H$, and the true ionic product is $K_c = 4\alpha^3 H^3$. Hence, $K_c = \alpha^3 K_H$. Thus, the relation between the electrometrically determined solubility product and the solubility product evaluated on the basis of gravimetric results—in which partial ionization has not been accounted for—in the case of hydroxides of bivalent metals, depends on the cube of the degree of ionization; and in hydroxides of trivalent and tetravalent metals it will depend on the 4th and 5th power of the degree of ionization respectively. In general, $K_c = K_H \alpha^{(V+1)}$, where $V =$ the valency of the metal in the metal hydroxide. It is therefore interesting to compare the results obtained electrometrically and analytically for some metal hydroxides.

Glasstone[34] determined the solubility product and solubility of red lead monoxide, the former by conductimetric measurements, the latter by analysis, as 1.17×10^{-15} and 0.26×10^{-3} respectively, both values being obtained at 25°C. He also pointed out that the determination of the solubility by the use of the solubility product determined conductimetrically was likely—in the absence of certainty as to the degree of ionization—to lead to incorrect results.

The solubility product of silver hydroxide has been determined by Britton[35,36]—using a silver electrode—as 1.50×10^{-8}, by Böttger,[37] using conductivity measurements, as 1.52×10^{-8}, and by Whitby[38] (by analysis) as 2.2×10^{-8} to 3.4×10^{-8}, the three values being for 20°C.

Further evidence for the existence of un-ionized metal hydroxides is available from the considerable work carried out on aquo-acids. Bjerrum[39] was probably the first to draw attention to their importance and to postulate that unpolymerized metal hydroxides resulted directly from the ionization of the hydrated metal ions. For the general case we may write

$$M(H_2O)_n^{x+} \rightleftharpoons xH^+ + M(H_2O)_{(n-x)}(OH)_x$$

It has been shown that this (aquo-acid) interpretation can be applied to the hydrated ferric[40,41], chromium[41,42], cobalt[42,43], aluminium[41], magnesium[44], calcium[45], copper[46,47,48,49], silver[50,51], zinc[52], mercury[53], and other ions.

The principle of partial ionization may be applied also to the precipitation and non-precipitation of sulphides in qualitative and quantitative analysis. In the case of cadmium sulphide, direct evidence is available to show the presence of un-ionized cadmium sulphide. The preferred values for the solubility product and solubility of cadmium sulphide given by Ravitz[54] are 1.14×10^{-28} (a higher value than those given by Bruner and Zawadsky[55,56]) and 1.46×10^{-10} respectively. Since in the case of 100 per cent ionization, the equation

$$\text{solubility} = \sqrt{\text{solubility product}}$$

gives the concentration of the ionized fraction for bi-bivalent salts, the concentration of the ionized cadmium sulphide is approximately 10^{-14}. Hence, the ionization of cadmium sulphide solutions is approximately 0.01 per cent. The possible significance of such small degrees of "ionization" extends to other topics.

It might be thought that the existence of "partial ionization" applies strictly to what are known as "weak" electrolytes, such as metal hydroxides stated above, but that "strong" electrolytes, such as NaCl, are completely "ionized" in solution. In favour of this standpoint it is usually quoted that strong electrolytes are completely dissociated in the solid state and that consequently they should be also completely dissociated in solution, particularly so because the process of solution utilizes the energy of hydration which *per se* requires separation of the ionic constituents. Indeed, any deviations of the experimental results—for example, colligative properties— have been attributed to interionic attraction effects resulting in reduced "activity" of these supposedly structurally independent ions. In certain cases the deviations were attributed to complex ion formation—owing to replacement of coordinated water of hydration —or to ion pairs. Such an interpretation may be further extended in terms of the following picture, advocated by the author, which involves *complete ionization* and *partial association via the associated water molecules*. For example,

Ionized and dissociated   *Ionized but undissociated*

The unit of so far as electrometric

measurements are concerned, can be reasonably expected to behave as a non-electrolyte having a high dipole moment value, such as is the case in the aminoacid zwitterion.

The proportion of such ionized, but undissociated—and therefore apparently non-electrolyte—units is bound to increase with the ratio charge/area of the respective ions and with decrease in temperature (since the thermal motion of the water molecules tends to break up such ionic associations). Such ionic associations could well be a major factor in the considerable experimental deviations of activity coefficient values of 2:2 and other electrolytes from these calculated on the basis of the Debye-Hückel equations.

The concept of the existence of such units may be integrated into an overall scheme of partial dissociation, such as in the case of cadmium sulphide,

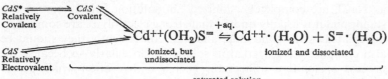

$$Cd^{++}(OH_2)S^= \leftrightharpoons Cd^{++} \cdot (H_2O) + S^= \cdot (H_2O)$$

The significance of the precipitation of non-stable forms is discussed later on. However, it should be possible to appreciate even at this stage that attainment of some of the equilibria is rather slow, and that the rate-determining step for the overall reaction is controlled by its slowest velocity constant. The greater the number of equilibria present, the greater are the number of steps and therefore the greater is the probability of encountering some very slow reactions. However, if ionic concentrations much higher than those calculated on the basis of the solubility product value are used, then formation of precipitate is more likely to take place immediately.

* The existence of two forms of solid cadmium sulphide have been noted by Bruner and Zawadsky[56] and by Milligan.[93] The former recorded that these two forms have different solubility product values, the latter that they have different crystalline forms. According to Glasstone[96] one form has the structural configuration of ZnO—which is relatively electrovalent, the other form has the structural configuration of ZnS which is relatively, if not purely, covalent. See also p. 77.

CHAPTER 7

Variation of Equilibrium Constants with Temperature

An equilibrium constant (K) varies with the absolute temperature (T) and heat of reaction (ΔH) according to the van't Hoff Equation

$$\frac{\mathrm{d}\log K}{\mathrm{d}T} = \frac{\Delta H}{2 \cdot 303 R T^2} \quad \cdot \quad \cdot \quad \cdot \quad (18)$$

or its integrated forms

$$\log \frac{K_2}{K_1} = \frac{\Delta H}{2 \cdot 303 R} \left\{ \frac{1}{T_1} - \frac{1}{T_2} \right\} \quad \cdot \quad \cdot \quad (19)$$

or

$$\log K = \frac{-\Delta H}{2 \cdot 303 R T} + C \quad \cdot \quad \cdot \quad \cdot \quad (20)$$

where R is the universal gas constant, the suffices 1 and 2 refer to the respective absolute temperatures, and C is an integration constant.

The variation of the equilibrium constant value with temperature depends therefore on both sign and magnitude of the heat of reaction. If ΔH is positive (that is, heat is absorbed), the value of K increases with temperature, while a negative heat of reaction (heat is evolved) results in decrease in its value with rise in temperature.* Graphically, the above can be represented as shown in Fig. 8.

Now, the solubilities, and therefore the solubility product values, of most sparingly soluble substances rise with rise in temperature. Consequently, the process of solution is generally endothermic—

* The convention adopted here is that heat evolved by the system represents a loss of energy from the system to the surroundings, and vice versa. This is generally used in all post-elementary teaching in chemistry.

37

that is, it requires the absorption of heat. Conversely, it is possible to assess whether the heat of solution is exothermic or endothermic by the use of a theoretical cycle, namely the Born cycle, and using this result it is possible to evaluate the variation of the solubility product with temperature change.

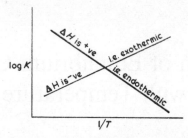

FIG. 8. VARIATION OF THE EQUILIBRIUM CONSTANT VALUE WITH TEMPERATURE

In this connexion it is pertinent to consider the variation in the ionic product of water with temperature. Water ionizes thus

$$H_2O \rightleftharpoons H^+ + OH^-$$

Hence,

$$\frac{(a_{H^+})(a_{OH^-})}{a_{H_2O}} = K$$

Rewriting we obtain

$$(a_{H^+})(a_{OH^-}) = K(a_{H_2O})$$

In very dilute solutions, say below 10^{-5}M, we may substitute concentrations for activities. Then

$$[H^+][OH^-] = K[H_2O]$$

In such ranges we can go further and assume that the concentration of water is practically constant because any amount that has combined with the ions of the electrolyte is minute compared to the overall water concentration—which, assuming a "molecular weight" of 18, is 1,000/18, i.e. about 55·5 moles per litre. And since the product of two constants is equal to another constant,

$$[H^+][OH^-] = K_W$$

and because of the above assumptions this ionic product of water, K_W, is also equal to the activity product $(a_{H^+})(a_{OH^-})$.

The above dissociation of water is endothermic having $\Delta H \simeq$ 13,700 cal/mole. Hence the value of the ionic product of water should rise with temperature. The variation of the product with temperature is given in Table 1.

TABLE 1[57]

VARIATION OF K_W WITH TEMPERATURE

Temperature °C	$K_W \times 10^{14}$
0	0·1133
5	0·1846
10	0·2920
15	0·4503
20	0·6809
25	1·008
30	1·468
35	2·089
40	2·917
45	4·018
50	5·474
55	7·297
60	9·614
100	56

Such a variation is of significance in the precipitation of sparingly soluble metal hydroxides. This precipitation can be represented in several ways. Taking the case of ferric hydroxide as an example,

$$Fe(OH)_3 \rightleftharpoons Fe^{+++} + 3OH^-$$
solid

or in the equivalent form including the water of hydration

$$Fe(OH)_3 + (b + 3c)H_2O \rightleftharpoons (Fe \cdot bH_2O)^{+++} + 3(OH \cdot cH_2O)^-$$

Alternatively the aquo-acid mode of representation may be utilized

$$Fe(OH)_3 + 3H_2O \rightleftharpoons (Fe^{+++} \cdot 3OH^- \cdot 3H_2O)^0$$
solid
$$+$$
$$3H^+$$
$$\Updownarrow$$
$$(Fe \cdot 6H_2O)^{+++}$$

The following treatment applies to very dilute solutions and with increase in ionic strength the assessment will become progressively less accurate. Either of the above approaches may be undertaken and the final result should be practically the same, since the comprehensive solubility product equation reduces to the concentration solubility product equation in very dilute solutions and since substitution of the correct dissociation constants lead to the same result. Representing the above in terms of the concentration solubility product, we have

$$[Fe^{+++}][OH^-]^3 = K_c$$

where the above ionic symbols represent the hydrated ions. Consequently,

$$[Fe^{+++}] = \frac{K_c}{[OH^-]^3}$$

Substituting in terms of the ionic product of water, we have

$$[Fe^{+++}] = \frac{K_c[H^+]^3}{(K_W)^3}$$

Hence, at a given pH the permissible $[Fe^{+++}]$ for precipitation to be considered possible is

$$[Fe^{+++}] \propto \frac{1}{(K_W)^3}$$

The value of K_W usually taken for calculation purposes is 1×10^{-14} but at room temperature which is often 15°C to 17°C, K_W is about 0.5×10^{-14}. This represents a variation of 50 per cent in the value of K_W and results, in the case of ferric hydroxide, in a percentage error of about $\{1/(0.5)^3\} \times 100 \cong 800$ per cent. Similar calculations can be carried out in other cases. It is seen therefore that approximations in the value of the ionic product of water can lead to appreciable errors.

CHAPTER 8

Lack of Equilibrium Conditions

It has already been pointed out that the solubility product principle can be derived for *stable equilibrium* conditions only. It cannot be stressed too often that an equilibrium constant can be applied correctly only under such conditions* and that the application of the solubility product principle to conditions which do not comply with the above requirements is bound to lead to inaccurate results. The further the actual conditions are from those of thermodynamic, stable, equilibrium, the less accurate are the results obtained from the applications of the principle and the greater is the error involved in the assumption that the calculated results are correct.

The application of the solubility product principle in chemical analysis has taken place in several ways of which the two most prominent ones are—

(a) Calculation of the solubility product values from precipitations of the corresponding substances under specified sets of conditions which were not stable equilibrium ones.

(b) Use of solubility product values—determined under stable equilibrium conditions—to calculate quantitatively the conditions of precipitation in the usual qualitative and quantitative analysis which ordinarily take place under non-equilibrium conditions.

Unfortunately it has rarely been pointed out that most of these calculations and assessments are highly approximate because they have been calculated for conditions to which they do not strictly apply. There seems to have been insufficient appreciation of the significance, in relation to the applicability of the solubility product principle, of the well-known fact that rapid precipitations favour the formation of non-stable states[82], or forms, and that

---

* Strictly speaking one should consider thermodynamic equilibrium conditions which involve, of course, mechanical, thermal and chemical equilibrium conditions.

considerable time may elapse while the original non-stable forms undergo a series of subsequent changes involving intermediate degrees of non-stability before the final, stable, equilibrium state is attained. To quote only a few of such well-known facts—

(*a*) The rapid mixing of concentrated solutions containing respectively barium and sulphate ions does not result in the formation of the stable crystalline variety of barium sulphate. Instead, the "precipitate" initially formed is a barium sulphate gel which changes only slowly into the stable crystalline variety[61].

(*b*) Rapid hydrolysis of salts such as ferric chloride—for example, by addition of a small quantity of ferric chloride to a large volume of boiling distilled water—does not result in the formation of the usual type of ferric hydroxide gelatinous precipitate, nor in the formation of the stable crystalline variety. Instead, a colloidal suspension of ferric hydroxide is obtained.

(*c*) Rapid precipitation of hydrated calcium tartrate results in the formation of the metastable form[98].

The pattern of formation of non-stable forms in rapid precipitations was recognized already in the nineteenth century. Bancroft[58] was one of the first to point out that "it appears as if the generalization may be made that when sudden precipitation occurs the least stable form is first to appear." Ostwald[59], in his empirical Law of Successive Transformations, attempted to formulate these phenomena in terms of a free energy pattern, thus: "When a given chemical system is left in an unstable state, it tends to change not into its most stable form but into the form of stability which most nearly resembles its own, i.e. in to that transient or stable modification whose formation from the original state is accompanied by the smallest loss in free energy."

The law was attacked by Tammann[60] who stressed that the type of nucleation encountered determines what type of metastable state is formed. Further assessment of the free energy pattern involved in the formation and disappearance of non-stable states in relation to the applicability of the solubility product principle will be considered later. However, whatever point of view may be favoured in the interpretation of these phenomena, there can be no doubt that rapid precipitations—such as those taking place in qualitative analysis— take place under conditions far removed from thermodynamic, stable, equilibrium conditions. It follows that the application of stable equilibrium constants, such as solubility products, to non-equilibrium conditions will result in inaccurate predictions. Any "agreement" between erroneously calculated values and experimental results is possible only where a considerable margin of error is possible. Fortunately, such large margins of error are possible in precipitations in qualitative analysis. For example, suppose we calculate (Lewin[12,17])—using the solubility product value of a given substance—that a given ionic product is the minimum required for "precipitation" (which would be the correct value under stable equilibrium conditions)—then for *immediate* precipitation it will be found necessary in practice, to have a minimum ionic concentration ratio $\dfrac{\text{ionic product}}{\text{solubility product}}$ of 10^3 to 10^5. For example, the solubility product of barium sulphate is about 10^{-10}. This means that when solutions containing barium and sulphate ions respectively are mixed, then—by the solubility product principle—the required product of the ionic concentrations in the mixtures should be such as to exceed the value of the solubility product. For convenience sake consider the mixing of equal volumes of solutions having the same concentrations. The minimum concentrations required then would be 10^{-5} g ions each of Ba^{++} and $SO_4^{=}$ per litre in the final solution; or 2×10^{-5} g ions each of Ba^{++} and $SO_4^{=}$ in the original solutions. In practice, much higher concentrations are required. Thus, Von Weimarn[61] noted that, in conditions involving mixing equal volumes of solutions having the same molarities, 2×10^{-4}N solutions of barium thiocyanate and manganese sulphate, giving an $\dfrac{\text{ionic product}}{\text{solubility product}}$ ratio equal to 25, the precipitate appeared only after about a month to a year. Even when the ratio was equal to 625—using 10^{-3}N solutions for mixing—the precipitate began appearing only after five to ten minutes, the precipitation continuing over a week. To obtain immediate precipitation, it was necessary to employ concentrations giving rise to $\dfrac{\text{ionic product}}{\text{solubility product}}$ ratios greater than about 1.5×10^4. Similar calculations by the author for several other electrolyte precipitations show that for immediate precipitation it is sometimes necessary to have values, for the above ionic precipitation ratio, which are greater than 10^4, but in other cases, the precipitation ratio may be much lower.

The above experimentally determined requirements can be explained in terms of absence of stable nuclei of the respective insoluble substances. It is well-known that supersaturated solutions once prepared—for example, supersaturated solution of sodium thiosulphate—can remain as such for considerable periods, but that addition of a crystal of the corresponding substance enhances, or results in, immediate precipitation. The comparative stability of the supersaturated solution, in absence of a stable nucleus, is attributed to the process of formation of a precipitate which proceeds from the initial attachment of a number of ions and adherence of other ions to it, resulting eventually in the formation of a particle sufficiently large to be precipitated out of suspension. In this process, the adherence of the ions results initially in the formation of exceedingly small particles which eventually form the larger ones. Now, the activity, or vapour pressure, of very small particles is greater than that of the corresponding large crystal and is given by the expression

$$\log \left\{ \frac{p_{(f.\,\text{solid})}}{p_{(\text{solid})}} \right\} = \log \left\{ \frac{a_{(f.\,\text{solid})}}{a_{(\text{solid})}} \right\} = \frac{2\sigma M}{2\cdot303 r d R T} \quad *$$

where the "p"s and "a"s represent the respective vapour pressures and activities, "*solid*" and "*f. solid*" represent the large crystals and fine crystals respectively, σ is the surface tension, M is the molecular weight, r is the radius of the fine particles, d is the density, R is the gas constant per mole, and T is the absolute temperature.

Now, for the process of precipitation to be noticed visually, the reversible reaction

$$\begin{array}{ccc} \text{Very fine} & + & \text{water} \\ \text{solid particles} & & \text{molecules} \end{array} \rightleftharpoons \begin{array}{c} \text{Hydrated} \\ \text{ions} \end{array}$$

and its associated comprehensive ionic product equation, namely—

$$(a_+)^x(a_-)^y = K(a_{(f.\,\text{solid})})(a_{H_2O})^{(xb+yc)}$$
ionic product

should apply before the final stable, equilibrium

$$\begin{array}{ccc} \text{Large} & + & \text{water} \\ \text{solid particles} & & \text{molecules} \end{array} \rightleftharpoons \begin{array}{c} \text{Hydrated} \\ \text{ions} \end{array}$$

and its associated comprehensive solubility product value namely—

$$(a_+)^x(a_-)^y = K(a_{\text{solid}})(a_{H_2O})^{(xb+yc)}$$
solubility
product

are finally attained.

Other things being equal, or practically equal, e.g. temperature and hydration,

$$\frac{\text{Ionic product}}{\text{Solubility product}} = \frac{a_{(f.\,\text{solid})}}{a_{(\text{solid})}} = \text{Antilog} \left\{ \frac{2\sigma M}{2\cdot303 r d R T} \right\}^* \quad (21)$$

The above formulation is highly approximate, because the crystals of ordinary electrolytes are not spherical; but it is indicative of the

* See p. 56.

type of calculation involved. Assuming the overall correctness of the above approach, it is possible to obtain a *highly approximate* estimate for the precipitation ratio for possible radii of crystal nuclei, using available surface tension data* by substitution into the above relationship. Thus, for a possible theoretical radius of 10^{-6} cm, we have for the precipitation ratio for $BaSO_4$, at 25°C—

$$\frac{\text{Ionic product}}{\text{Solubility product}} \approx$$

$$\text{Antilog}\left\{\frac{2 \times 3,000 \text{ dynes/cm} \times 233 \text{ g/mol.}}{2\cdot303 \times 10^{-6} \text{ cm} \times 4\cdot5 \text{ g/cm}^3 \times 8\cdot314 \atop \times 10^7 \text{ ergs/deg. mol.} \times 298 \text{ deg.}}\right\}$$

$$\approx 3 \times 10^5$$

If, however, the surface tension value be taken as 1,500 dynes/cm the above precipitation ratio $\approx 6 \times 10^2$. The experimentally determined value, namely about $1\cdot5 \times 10^4$, lies between the above two calculated values.

In view of the possible considerable variation of surface tension with type, and concentration, of the dissolved electrolyte and of the radius of the nucleus, it is not surprising to find that the precipitation ratio varies considerably from one electrolyte precipitation to another.

The large precipitation ratios possible, and the smaller ones existing in other electrolytes, may be the major contributory factor to the lack of precipitation encountered in several cases in qualitative analysis. For example, NiS and ZnS have solubility product values sufficiently low to be precipitable in Group II in the presence of about $0\cdot5N$ HCl. Yet, as is well-known, they are not precipitated there. However, solutions of zinc and nickel salts, in presence of $0\cdot5N$ HCl and saturated with H_2S, if allowed to stand for some time—days or weeks—give rise to the corresponding sulphide precipitates. In view of the fact that precipitation does take place eventually, it cannot be assumed that its initial lack was due to stable complex formation or low percentage of dissociation, and the precipitation ratio may well account for the phenomenon. Thus, in the case of ZnS, in presence of $0\cdot5N$ HCl and saturated H_2S we have

$$[H^+] = 0\cdot5; \quad f_{H+} \cong 0\cdot75\dagger; \quad [H_2S] = 0\cdot1 \cong a_{H_2S},$$

---

* According to Dundon,[62] the value of the interfacial tension of $BaSO_4/H_2O$ is 3,000 dynes per cm. Hullet,[63] however, gives the value as 1,500 dynes per cm.

† f_{H+} in $0\cdot5N$ HCl is $0\cdot757$; but the presence of other electrolytes affects this value to an uncertain extent.

since H_2S is a non-electrolyte.

$$K_{H_2S} = \frac{(a_{H^+})^2 a_{S^=}}{a_{H_2S}} \cong 10^{-22}; \quad K_{ZnS} = a_{Zn^{++}} \times a_{S^=} \cong 10^{-26}$$

When *stable* equilibrium has been attained,

$$a_{Zn^{++}} \cong \frac{K_{ZnS}}{a_{S^-}}^* = \frac{10^{-26}}{a_{S^-}} \approx \frac{10^{-26}}{7 \times 10^{-23}} \cong 1\cdot4 \times 10^{-4}$$

No data are available for the activity coefficient values of zinc ions in the above solution. However, making the highly approximate assumption that the activity coefficient of the Zn^{++} ion in the above solution is the same as that of a zinc chloride solution having an equivalent ionic strength, we have $f_{Zn^{++}} \approx 0.35$. Hence,

$$[Zn^{++}] \approx \frac{1\cdot4 \times 10^{-4}}{0\cdot35} \approx 4 \times 10^{-4} \text{ moles per litre}$$

and since the solution contains 0·1 moles per litre, precipitation should take place readily. However, as precipitation can be observed only after some time, the initial failure to precipitate may well be attributed to the lack of thermodynamic, stable, equilibrium conditions which is associated with a precipitation ratio *greater* than $\frac{0\cdot1}{4 \times 10^{-4}}$, that is, greater than 250.

It should, however, be remembered that the above calculation did not allow for the presence of ionized, but undissociated, and covalent forms of zinc sulphide in solution. When allowance is made for these, the precipitation ratio is bound to be greater than the above assessed value. Further the implicit assumption that $f_{H^+} = (f_+)_{HCl}$ may not be sufficiently accurate (see p. 85).

---

* Strictly speaking, the *comprehensive* solubility product equation should be used. Therefore, this is a highly approximate calculation.

CHAPTER 9

The Significance of the Solubility Product in Non-stable Conditions

THE failure to attain equilibrium within one particular phase, or both phases in contact, results in absence of equilibrium for the system solid-solution as a whole. That equilibrium may not be readily attained within the liquid phase can be easily appreciated because solutions of many electrolytes, in absence of the solid phase, show continuous variations in certain properties. Thus, solutions of ammonium stannic chloride, zinc sulphate, ferric sulphate or of other salts, on standing after preparation, develop increasing hydrogen ion concentrations, and in some cases precipitation may take place. This behaviour may be attributed to the hydrolysis of the aquo-acid metal ion, or some other change in the constitution of the co-ordinated metal ion. Whatever the explanation, some time may elapse—in some cases several days or weeks—before true equilibrium conditions have been attained. The same behaviour takes place in presence of the solid phase, and consequently stable equilibrium conditions in the system solid ⇌ solution are not attainable for some time; and until such time, the solubility product equations (involving a stable equilibrium between stable solids and stable solutions) are not strictly applicable. Slow as the attainment of equilibrium in the liquid phase may be, we may expect, on the whole, the attainment of equilibrium conditions within the solid phase to be much slower because of the considerably restricted ionic and molecular movements taking place in the latter. It may therefore be reasonably assumed that the rate-determining factor in the establishment of thermodynamic, stable, equilibrium is the achievement of equilibrium in the solid phase.

A solid form of a substance—which is capable of further spontaneous change in size, form or composition at constant temperature

47

and pressure—may appear to be in equilibrium with its "saturated" solution, because though its chemical potential is changing, the change is taking place so slowly that it may appear negligible, and hence a_{solid} appears constant. This apparent equilibrium can be shown to be temporary, because eventually some physical or chemical change can be noted. True equilibrium will be attained only when the sum of the respective chemical potentials involved in the forward reaction is equal to that involved in the reverse reaction. Until then the conditions must be regarded as non-stable, and any "solubility product" evaluated from such conditions should be referred to as a *non-stable* solubility product. A non-stable solubility product cannot have the same value as the stable solubility product at the same temperature and pressure any more than a stable solubility product for a given electrolyte and set of conditions for one temperature is likely to have the same value for a different temperature, under otherwise equal conditions, for the simple reason that the condition of equality of the forward and reverse sums of chemical potentials is no longer obeyed. It follows, of course, that the application of the stable solubility product value to non-stable conditions, where a non-stable solid is involved, is theoretically unsound. Thus, the application of the *stable* solubility product values, evaluated under stable equilibrium conditions employing the stable crystalline varieties, to precipitation of gelatinous precipitates as has been generally carried out—in Group III of qualitative analysis—is erroneous.

There are many types of non-stable states which may be formed in chemical analysis. Such types and likely sequences are given in Fig. 9.

Any of the above intermediate states can be considered non-stable when it can be shown that after a time interval the physical or chemical properties of the state have been altered. Such changes have been demonstrated in a considerable number of the various states arising out of electrolyte precipitation, but only a few cases can be considered here.

(*a*) *Colloid Formation.* Lyophobic suspensions, in many cases, represent a class of non-stable conditions where the suspended colloid, owing to its very small size, possesses a very large ratio of surface to volume and hence a very high surface free-energy content. Under suitable conditions, such as the absence of traces of foreign salts, or given sufficient time, the suspended lyophobe will precipitate giving rise to crystals of the pure substance, while coagulation on addition of sufficient quantities of other electrolytes results in a precipitate containing the adsorbed, precipitating electrolyte.

Whatever path is employed, the suspended colloid, though capable of prolonged apparent stability, is in a non-stable state since eventually precipitation will take place accompanied by considerable decrease in the free energy content of the system.

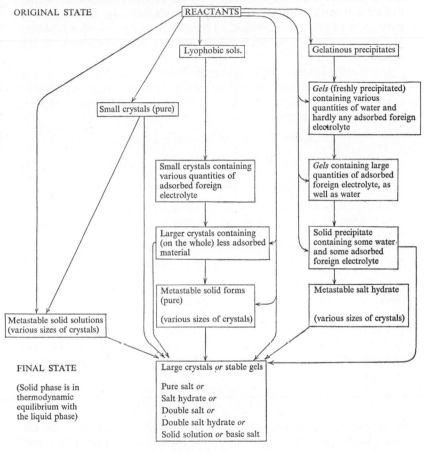

ORIGINAL STATE   REACTANTS

Lyophobic sols.

Gelatinous precipitates

Small crystals (pure)

Gels (freshly precipitated) containing various quantities of water and hardly any adsorbed foreign electrolyte

Small crystals containing various quantities of adsorbed foreign electrolyte

Gels containing large quantities of adsorbed foreign electrolyte, as well as water

Larger crystals containing (on the whole) less adsorbed material

Solid precipitate containing some water and some adsorbed foreign electrolyte

Metastable solid forms (pure)

(various sizes of crystals)

Metastable salt hydrate

(various sizes of crystals)

Metastable solid solutions (various sizes of crystals)

FINAL STATE

(Solid phase is in thermodynamic equilibrium with the liquid phase)

Large crystals *or* stable gels

Pure salt *or*
Salt hydrate *or*
Double salt *or*
Double salt hydrate *or*
Solid solution *or* basic salt

FIG. 9

(*b*) *Gels.* The equilibrium

gel ⇌ surrounding solution

is a non-stable equilibrium whenever the freshly precipitated gel shows physical changes with the passage of time. In general, freshly precipitated inorganic gels such as those of aluminium hydroxide, ferric hydroxide, chromium hydroxide and others undergo continuously decreasing changes in solubility by alkalis, peptizability and adsorption capacity; X-ray diffraction patterns which, at the beginning, are very diffuse eventually show interference lines which are associated with the formation of larger units from the smaller ones constituting the gel structure. Simultaneously, the degree of hydration of the gel decreases. These changes, being spontaneous, are accompanied by a decrease in the free energy content of the system.

(c) *Small Crystals.* It is generally known that small crystals, if allowed to stay in contact with a solvent in which they are soluble —even to a very slight extent—will grow into large ones. Hence, the apparent equilibrium

$$\text{small crystals} \rightleftharpoons \text{saturated solution}$$

is really a non-stable equilibrium in which the reaction

$$\text{small crystals} \rightarrow \text{large crystals}$$

is taking place spontaneously and continuously.

(d) *Adsorption.* The apparent equilibrium

$$\begin{array}{l}\text{freshly precipitated} \\ \text{contaminated solid}\end{array} \rightleftharpoons \begin{array}{l}\text{saturated} \\ \text{solution}\end{array}$$

is a non-stable equilibrium, as it can be shown that the solid phase undergoes continuous changes in composition with the passage of time.

The freshly contaminated solid may be a non-stable solid solution or merely contain adsorbed layers of impurities around the precipitated particles. The latter is often the case. The continuous process

$$\begin{array}{l}\text{freshly precipitated} \\ \text{contaminated solid}\end{array} \rightarrow \begin{array}{l}\text{stable, final,} \\ \text{state}\end{array}$$

is accompanied by considerable decrease in surface area of the precipitated particles which have not formed a proper crystal and are often separated by fine layers of water. Such decrease in surface area is accompanied by decrease in free energy content of the system. Generally, the greater the surface area, the greater is the degree of adsorption, as the latter takes place on the surface. Consequently, the decrease in surface area must be accompanied by decrease in content of adsorbed material. The preliminary adsorption of material from the solution during the actual precipitation can be appreciated from the fact that on shaking finely divided solids with electrolyte solutions, considerable adsorption may take place. Thus, Hullett and Duschak[64] have shown that barium chloride was taken up not only during the precipitation of barium sulphate, but also when finely divided barium sulphate crystals were suspended in barium chloride solution, whereas the shaking of large crystals of barium sulphate with the chloride solution showed no perceptible adsorption by the former. A more comprehensive investigation was carried out by Johnson and Adams[65] into the uptake of various ions by barium sulphate. They concluded that the generally termed "occlusion" was an adsorption phenomenon which depended on

(i) the magnitude of the concentration of the original solution,

(ii) the initial fineness of the precipitate, and

(iii) the amount of recrystallization which has taken place.

APPENDIX 1

Thermodynamic Derivation of the Comprehensive Solubility Product Equation

CONSIDER a solid substance such as M_xA_y in equilibrium with saturated solution. The solid may be assumed to have a constant, though small, vapour pressure—or fugacity*—because equilibrium conditions have been established. The equilibrium may be written in terms of a solid electrolyte or solid covalent compound which only ionizes on association with water molecules, or in some intermediate way. It makes no difference to the derivation of the principle. For simplicity only two possibilities will be shown.

$$
\left.
\begin{array}{c}
\textit{Solid} \quad \textit{Vapour} \\
M_xA_y \rightleftharpoons M_xA_y \\
+ \\
(xb + yc)H_2O \\
\Updownarrow \\
xM^{z+} \cdot bH_2O \\
+ \\
yM^{z-} \cdot cH_2O
\end{array}
\right\}
\begin{array}{l}
\textit{Saturated} \\
\textit{Solution}
\end{array}
$$

$$
\left.
\begin{array}{c}
\textit{Solid} \qquad \textit{Vapour} \\
xM^{z+} \cdot yA^{z-} \rightleftharpoons xM^{z+} \cdot yA^{z-} \\
+ \\
(xb + yc)H_2O \\
\Updownarrow \\
xM^{z+} \cdot bH_2O \\
+ \\
yA^{z-} \cdot cH_2O
\end{array}
\right\}
\begin{array}{l}
\textit{Saturated} \\
\textit{Solution}
\end{array}
$$

* Fugacity may be defined in this connexion as the tendency of the vapour to escape from the solid.

52

The heterogeneous equilibrium between the solid and the saturated solution depends on or is associated with a homogeneous equilibrium in solution. Thermodynamically this represents a closed system in which the chemical potential of the solid phase must be equal to that of its vapour in solution and where, in the saturated solution, the sum of the chemical potentials for the forward reaction must equal those for the reverse reaction. Consequently, we may write

$$\mu_{solid} + (xb + yc)\mu_{(H_2O)} = x\mu_+ + y\mu_-$$

where μ_+ and μ_- represent respectively the chemical potentials of the *hydrated* cation and anion.

Therefore,

$$\mu^0_{(solid)} + RT \ln (a_{solid}) + (xb + yc)[\mu^0_{(H_2O)} + RT \ln (a_{H_2O})]$$
$$= x[\mu^0_+ + RT \ln (a_+)] + y[\mu^0_- + RT \ln (a_-)]$$

Rearranging, we obtain

$$\mu^0_{(solid)} + (xb + yc)\mu^0_{(H_2O)} - (x\mu^0_+ + y\mu^0_-) = xRT \ln (a_+) + yRT \ln (a_-)$$

$$- \left[\begin{matrix} (xb + yc)RT \ln (a_{H_2O}) \\ + RT \ln (a_{solid}) \end{matrix} \right]$$

$$= RT \ln \frac{(a_+)^x (a_-)^y}{(a_{solid})(a_{H_2O})^{(xb+yc)}}$$

Now, the standard chemical potentials are, by definition, constant quantities, at constant temperature and constant external pressure for the species concerned, x and y are constant, and assuming that b and c remain constant, the left-hand side of the above equation is constant. Dividing both sides by RT and taking antilogarithms of the resulting equation, the left-hand side becomes another constant (since the logarithm of a constant is also constant) say K, and the result is

$$K = \frac{(a_+)^x (a_-)^y}{(a_{solid})(a_{H_2O})^{(xb+yc)}}$$

which is, of course, identical with equation (9).

Solid Activity

THE existence of polymorphic and allotropic forms of elements and compounds has been appreciated for a considerable time; but the main emphasis, until recent times, has been on their temperature and pressure relationships. It has also been shown that variations in the conditions of deposition or preparation of a given element or compound can result, at constant temperature and external pressure, in the formation of different crystalline or amorphous forms— having the same stoichiometric composition. The deposition of other forms than that of the stable variety has been attributed to the formation of metastable forms which, once isolated, owed their apparent stability to an extremely slow rate of reaction taking place in the solid phase. It was also appreciated that the resulting deposits often had variable, and therefore non-stoichiometric, compositions. These were often attributed, sometimes correctly, to the formation of solid solutions whose variable free energy content is a function of their composition. However, even in those cases where it was accepted that the precipitate had indeed a variable composition, and where a solubility product was involved, it was assumed that the activity of the solid is a constant quantity in spite of its variable composition. Thus, in general, the concept of a constant activity of the specified solid—at constant temperature and external pressure—provided it was a perfect specimen, i.e. not strained or deformed, was held to be correct.* It was further assumed that this constant quantity was independent of the composition of the surrounding solution, and this principle was utilized in the derivation of the activity solubility product.

* See, for example, Glasstone, S., *Thermodynamics for Chemists*, D. Van Nostrand Co. Inc., New York, 1947, p. 398: "The activity of the solid salt at atmospheric pressure is taken as unity, by convention."

54

The survival of this belief is due to several factors, the most prominent of which are—

(*a*) The emphasis on temperature and pressure considerations to the neglect of other factors. Such neglect may be attributed to the fact that, in origin and development, classical thermodynamics was mainly devoted to gaseous equilibria, and there the most important considerations are those of temperature and pressure. But even in gases, surface energy considerations need not play a negligible part, as they may modify the activity of the gas to a noticeable extent; though the magnitude depends on the attractive forces between the gas and the surrounding vessel, which in turn depends on the respective polarities of the gas and the containing vessel.

(*b*) The concept of *chemical* compounds in which the stoichiometric ratio was deemed the most important test of compound formation or existence. This factor, when used as a criterion of purity of a compound, was of primary importance in the days of collection of data; preparation of compounds and their classification were considered the work of the day. Now, however, it is realized that the existence of any forms, physical or chemical, is determined by free energy considerations. The free energy contents, when influenced by lattice considerations, may result in the existence of well defined compounds. But the existence of such compounds— due to their minimal free energy contents under specified conditions —cannot justifiably be interpreted as a proof that their free energy contents are fixed quantities, at constant temperature and constant external pressure, independent of the composition of the surrounding solution.

Let us consider several arguments which show that the activity of a given solid is capable of continuous variation in its free energy content, despite the imposition of rigorous control of temperature and external pressure.

(1) THE EFFECT OF SUBDIVISION ON THE FREE ENERGY CONTENT OF A SOLID AT CONSTANT TEMPERATURE AND PRESSURE

The vapour pressure of a definite allotrope or polymorph, at constant temperature and external pressure*—and in the absence of extraneous vapours—is nowadays taken as constant. Nevertheless it is agreed that decrease in particle size is accompanied by increase in vapour pressure, and solubility, owing to the increase in surface free energy content. Since particle size is a continuously variable function, it follows that the free energy or the activity of a solid is a

---

* The external pressure is kept constant by introducing an inert gas until the overall pressure is at the required value, say one atmosphere.

continuously variable function, even at constant temperature and external pressure.

(2) THE EFFECT OF ADSORPTION OR COHESION ON THE FREE ENERGY CONTENT OF A SOLID, AT CONSTANT TEMPERATURE AND EXTERNAL PRESSURE

Consider the activity of a given solid in the following states—

(α) Let the standard state of the solid be that of the pure solid surrounded by its own vapour, in absence of physically or chemically interacting vapours, solids or liquids. Let the activity of the solid be a_α.

(β) Introduce a non-inert vapour into the space surrounding the solid—but keep the total external pressure constant by varying the quantity of inert gas originally present. Assume that when equilibrium has been attained, the vapour is adsorbed to some extent on the surface of the solid. This change is accompanied by the free energy change of the reaction of adsorption. Consequently the activity—as well as the free energy—of the solid must have changed. Let the new solid activity be a_β.

(γ) Introduce a liquid which is capable of wetting the surface of the solid in its standard state. Assume that the solid is insoluble in the surrounding liquid. As a result of the cohesion of some of the liquid on to the solid surface some free energy change must have taken place, and therefore the activity of the solid must have altered. Let the new activity be a_γ.

(δ) Let the solid be soluble to some extent in the surrounding liquid. Then the final free energy content and the activity of the solid, in this case, cannot be the same as in the previous case. Let the new activity of the solid be a_δ.

Several more variations can be attempted, but there is no point in giving further examples. The important point is that the free energy changes that have taken place in the various examples are unlikely to have the same value,

$$a_\alpha \neq a_\beta \neq a_\gamma \neq a_\delta$$

(3) THE EFFECT OF SURFACE TENSION AND DIELECTRIC CONSTANT ON THE ACTIVITY OF A SOLID, ON THE SOLUBILITY, AND ON THE SOLUBILITY PRODUCT VALUE

Consider the well-known Ostwald-Freundlich equation[66],[67],[68]

$$S_r/S_o = \text{antilog} \left(\frac{2\sigma M}{2 \cdot 303 r d R T} \right) \qquad . \qquad . \quad (22)$$

where the solubilities of the single solute in saturated solutions in contact with small particles having a radius r and those having a flat surface, e.g. large crystals, in contact with the solution, are given respectively by S_r and S_o, σ is the surface tension, M is the molecular weight of the substance and d is its density; R is the gas constant and T is the absolute temperature. Other factors being equal, this equation means that the solubility of a substance increases exponentially with rise in the value of the surface tension; or that decrease in particle radius results in increase in solubility. Consider the surface tension factor first. The activity of a solid is altered on changing the value of the interfacial tension between itself and the surrounding medium; other things being equal, decrease in surface tension results in decreased solid activity and consequently decreased solubility. It is significant therefore that traces of substances which have no structural or morphological similarity to sodium chloride, but which lowered the surface tension of the surrounding medium, have been shown to change the "crystal habit" of the salt. Milone and Ferrero[78] and Bunn[79] have shown that when sodium chloride is precipitated from its solution on addition of substances that reduced the surface tension, both octahedral and cubic forms—or only octahedral forms—of the crystals were formed, provided the surface tension was reduced to a value below 60 dynes per cm. Consider now the factor of subdivision. It is, of course, known that the vapour pressure of a given solid increases perceptibly with considerable decrease in particle radius; and since the vapour pressure of a solid may be taken as representing its activity, decrease in particle size signifies increase in solid activity and therefore increase in solubility. This has been confirmed by Hullett's findings that finer particles of gypsum or barium sulphate possess greater solubilities than the coarse ones by as much as 80 per cent. Parallel findings have been noted in other cases.

The Ostwald-Freundlich equation does not take into consideration possible ionic dissociation of the solid in solution nor the formation of an electrical double layer around the solid particle. A correction for the first factor has been introduced into the equation by Dundon and Mack.[69] The second factor has been allowed for by Knapp[70] who has modified the Ostwald-Freundlich equation to allow for the effect of any charge on the particles and the dielectric constant of the medium on the solubility of the solid. Thus

$$S_r/S_o = \text{antilog}\left\{\frac{M}{2\cdot303RT}\left[\frac{2\sigma}{rd} - \frac{Q^2\delta}{4\epsilon dr^5}\right]\right\} \qquad . \quad (23)$$

where ϵ is the dielectric constant of the medium, $Q =$ the electrical charge on each layer (of the Helmholtz double layer) of the solid liquid interface, $\delta =$ the distance between the layers. May and

The Solubility Product Principle

Kolthoff[71] adopted the general development by Knapp to the derivation of the following expression which substitutes the normal activity solubility product (K)—that is, that associated with large crystals—for the normal solubility, and K_r, the activity solubility product of the finely divided particles having radius r for the corresponding solubility, thus

$$K_r/K = \text{antilog} \left\{ \frac{M}{2 \cdot 303 RT} \left[\frac{2\sigma}{rd} - \frac{Q^2 \delta}{4\epsilon dr^5} \right] \right\} \qquad . \qquad (24)$$

Either of the above equations can be easily rewritten or proved in the form of vapour pressure relationships; that is, the left-hand side of the above equations can be replaced by (p/p_o) where p is the vapour pressure of small crystals having radius r, and p_o is the vapour pressure of the corresponding large crystals. Thus, we see that the activity of the solid phase can be affected by the degree of adsorption on its surface as well as by radius size, surface tension and variation in the value of the dielectric constant of the medium—which, of course, takes place with increase of ionic strength.

Ionic Strength

THE attractive forces between oppositely charged ions result in a tendency for them to associate. The overall picture may be drawn in terms neglecting the associated water molecules—as is often done in the current literature—or in terms involving them, as advocated in this book. Whatever picture is preferred, the overall result of such forces is a decrease in freedom of independent ionic movements as well as a decrease in the attractive or repulsive forces towards other ions. Accurate calculation or assessment of these effects is highly complicated and out of place here. However, it can be appreciated, even at this stage, that the magnitudes of both ionic concentration and charge are bound to play their part. Lewis and Randall[16] suggested the use of the function of "ionic strength" as a measure of the intensity of the electrical field which exists in a given solution. They defined it as equal to half the sum of all the respective products of the molalities (or molarities) of each ion in solution multiplied by the squares of their respective charges. Presented in the form of mathematical equations,

$$I_m = \tfrac{1}{2}\Sigma m_i z_i^2 \qquad . \quad . \quad . \quad (25)$$

and

$$I_c = \tfrac{1}{2}\Sigma c_i z_i^2 \qquad . \quad . \quad . \quad (26)$$

where I_m = the ionic strength expressed in terms of molalities and I_c = the ionic strength expressed in terms of molarities, c_i and m_i represent the respective ionic molarities or molalities, and z_i represents the respective ionic charges.

In dilute solutions, such as 0·1M, $I_m \cong I_c$.

The summation of the various ionic species for the calculation of ionic strength can be seen from the following examples—

The molal ionic strength of a uni-univalent electrolyte, such as NaCl is

$$I_m = \tfrac{1}{2}\Sigma(m \times 1^2) + (m \times 1^2) = m$$

The molal ionic strength of a uni-bivalent electrolyte such as Na_2SO_4 is

$$I_m = \tfrac{1}{2}\Sigma(\underset{(Na^+)}{2m \times 1^2}) + (\underset{(SO_4^=)}{m \times 2^2}) = 3m$$

The molal ionic strength of a solution containing 0·1 molal HBr and 0·5 molal calcium bromide is

$$I_m = \tfrac{1}{2}\{(\underset{(Ca^{++})}{0·5 \times 2^2}) + (\underset{(H^+)}{0·1 \times 1^2}) + (\underset{(Br^-)}{1·1 \times 1^2})\} = 1·6$$

The significance of the "ionic strength" lies in the present general acceptance of Lewis and Randall's generalization that in dilute solutions the activity coefficients of strong electrolytes are the same in all solutions of the same ionic strength. Experimentally, for 1:1 electrolytes, this range of dilution extends to practically $I = 0·01$, but is much lower for higher valency combinations. The agreement obtained in the former case is within 1 per cent for many of the 1:1 electrolytes, though somewhat greater variations are occasionally noted. See the Activity Coefficient Tables in Appendix 4.

It should be pointed out that the above evaluation of ionic strength may lead to erroneous predictions unless interfering factors are taken into consideration—for example, partial ionization and complex formation such as that taking place in cadmium iodide solutions namely, $2CdI_2 \rightleftharpoons Cd^{++}CdI_4^=$.

A possible objection to the accepted belief that the ionic strength is a comparatively accurate measure of the intensity of the electrical field in solution may be raised. It is not just the charge on the ion which matters, but rather the intensity or charge distribution of the field at the surface of the ion—that is the ratio, charge/(surface area). Accurate calculation of such factors is complicated by the difficulty in assessment of the ionic diameter in which allowance should be made for the presence of associated water molecules. There is no doubt that the dielectric constant value of the associated water molecules must be greater than that of pure water and that it increases with the ratio charge/(surface area of the *anhydrous* ion). Evidence for this standpoint is experimentally available. Consider, for example, the equivalent conductivities at infinite dilution of the alkali metal series from $Li^+ \rightarrow Cs^+$. The respective metal ion equivalent conductivities increase along this series, despite the possession of an identical, single, charge. This has been explained as being due to larger sized ions having weaker electrical fields at their periphery and therefore *smaller* numbers of attached dipole water molecules resulting in a smaller viscous drag under the same potential gradient. Consequently, equal ionic strength values—calculated by the above ionic strength definitions—of say, Li^+ or Cs^+ ions will not really represent equal magnitudes of electrical field intensity in solutions.

APPENDIX 4

Dipole Moments*

THE term dipole moment may be considered as the electric moment possessed by the particular molecule. To understand the significance of the term it is necessary to view the background of valency formulation. This formulation involves classification into the main groups of covalency, electrovalency and subgroups such as coordinate valency. However, these divisions, particularly the first two, may overlap. Thus, the distinction between electrovalency and covalency may become progressively less clear-cut on following a series of suitable atom pairs.

The bond between a pair of atoms can be represented in terms of electron give and take or electron sharing. One pattern which has been found convenient and useful to adopt in explaining bond formation is that of the tendency to form an electron pair (duplet) or an eight electron shell (octet). At first sight it would appear surprising that electrons should associate at all, as owing to their like charges they should repel one another. One explanation given is that the two electrons, constituting the single bond, spin in opposite directions and consequently give rise to attractive electromagnetic forces much greater than the electrical repulsion forces. These electromagnetic forces, while responsible for the attachment of electrons from different atoms and thus causing the chemical bond, do not, however, decide the actual position of the bonding electrons in relation to the bonded atoms. The relative magnitude of the positive charges on the nuclei of the two bonded atoms is mainly responsible for the "placing" of the electron pair, and it is this placing of the electrons which decides the type of valency formed. At the one extreme we have electrovalency where the two electrons are within the shell of only

---

* For a more extensive account see, for example, J. W. Smith, *Dipole Moments* (Butterworth, 1955).

one of the two atoms, namely the acceptor atom, while at the other extreme the two electrons are equally shared giving rise to simple covalency. Thus, when one atom is highly electronegative, while the other is highly electropositive—e.g. Cl and Na in sodium chloride; Br and K in potassium bromide—the bond is electrovalent. When the two atoms are identical—e.g. H:H; Cl:Cl; N:::N—the electrons making up the bond are equally attracted between the nuclei of the two atoms, and being equally shared, form a simple covalent bond. But when the two nuclei possess different numbers of positive charges, the two "shared" electrons are no longer equally shared; they are attracted somewhat more strongly towards the more positively charged nucleus.* This results in their being displaced nearer to the more positively charged nucleus than would be the case if the two nuclei were equally charged, when the electron pair would be midway between the two. Such a bond is considered to be a covalent bond because the electron pair is still being shared. However, the displacement of the electron pair from the "middle" position results in the centres of gravity of the negative and positive charges of the atoms involved in the linkage, no longer coinciding as they would had the two nuclei possessed the same number of positive charges. As a result, the bond is associated with a dipole moment which may be considered in terms of the polarity now possessed by the bond (i.e. δ^+ and δ^-) and the distance (d) between the two poles created, viz. $(\delta \times d)$. However, we need not concern ourselves with the actual values of these individual factors, but only with the value of the dipole moment itself, since the latter is a direct measure of the polarized state of the bond. It should be noted that the greater the value of the dipole moment, the less purely covalent is the bond; in the extreme case the bond becomes electrovalent.

Consider the water molecule. The number of positive charges on the oxygen nucleus is eight, on the hydrogen nucleus one. Consequently each electron pair making up the bond between the oxygen and the hydrogen atom is displaced towards the former giving it a negative polarity and each hydrogen atom a positive polarity, thus—

* This attraction is also affected by the atomic radius. For a given charge, the greater the atomic radius, the weaker is the field at the atom's surface. This results in a weaker attraction for the electron pair, e.g., the dipole moment of H_2S is smaller than that of H_2O. A more accurate assessment may be obtained in terms of electronegativity of the elements.

Water is therefore a covalent molecule having a high dipole moment value. And since dipole molecules may be expected to associate in the same way that magnets do, thus—

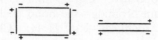

we may expect some degree of association between the dipole ends of the water molecules.

Activity and Activity Coefficients

THE terms "activity" and "activity coefficient" owe their existence to the fact that electrolyte solutions do not obey the Law of Mass Action when it is written in terms of concentrations. This may be summarized in Dawson's words[72]—

"The deviation of actual from ideal behaviour may be conveniently expressed by an activity coefficient (γ = ratio of activity to concentration), which may be defined as the factor by which the concentrations must be multiplied in order to make the expressions for mass action and free energy applicable to actual as distinguished from ideal solutes."

It will therefore be realized that the equation

activity = concentration × activity coefficient

is essentially empirical in origin. For this reason it was regarded by many with suspicion. However, the theoretical work of Debye and Hückel has resulted in their well-known limiting equations for the calculation of activity coefficient values over the approximate range of $I = 0$ to $I = 0\cdot1$. Hence over this range, the activity coefficient cannot justifiably be regarded as a purely empirical concept.

A simple picture involving ionic activities can be drawn as follows—

In a given electrolyte solution, the oppositely charged ions tend to attract one another with the result that their movements are no longer as independent as they would be in the absence of the electrostatic attractive forces. The greater the magnitudes of the opposite charges on the respective ions, the greater is their mutual attraction. Also, the greater the concentration, the nearer the ions are to one another and therefore the more effective is the mutual attraction. In general the greater the mutual attraction, the smaller is the degree of independence of ionic movements and the greater is the degree of association of ions to form ionic pairs, which for practical purposes behave as a single entity. Generally speaking, the "activity" of an ion is proportional to its degree of freedom—that is, of independent movement, so that an increase in the magnitude of the charge and of the concentration should decrease the activity coefficient value. This is generally the case as the electrolyte concentration is increased from zero. However, with sufficient increase in concentration the change in the magnitude of activity coefficient with concentration is decreased and eventually a reversal sets in; that is, the activity coefficient now increases with further rise in concentration; and in those cases where the solubility range is sufficiently high, it becomes higher than unity. This reversal eventually ending in an activity coefficient *greater than unity* might appear puzzling. However, the phenomenon may be covered in relatively simple terms by attributing it to inaccurate methods of expressing concentrations. In evaluating aqueous concentrations one employs the expression of number of moles per litre of solution (i.e. molarity), or per 1,000 grammes of water (i.e. molality). Now, when electrolytes are dissolved in water, they associate or combine with water molecules. If, therefore, one takes a certain quantity of water, say 1,000 grammes, and dissolves in it a certain quantity of the electrolyte, say n moles, which in solution are associated with, say, w grammes of water per mole of electrolyte, then strictly speaking the concentration is $\dfrac{n}{1,000 - nw}$ moles of solute per gramme of water, because the *free* water in which the hydrated solute electrolyte is dissolving is $(1,000 - nw)$ grammes. Now, while the solution is very dilute—that is, when n is very small—the factor nw is practically negligible compared to 1,000 and therefore one can write $\dfrac{n}{1,000 - nw} \cong \dfrac{n}{1,000}$ with only a slight error. However, as the electrolyte concentration is increased—that is, as n increases—nw increases too and becomes increasingly more significant with respect to 1,000. Consequently, it is no longer justifiable to substitute $\dfrac{n}{1,000}$ for $\dfrac{n}{1,000 - nw}$. Nevertheless this is done universally, because of the uncertainty concerning the exact value of w. Now, the value of the activity coefficient is calculated from the experimentally determined value of the activity by writing

$$\text{activity coefficient} = \frac{\text{activity}}{\text{concentration}}$$

The correct definition of the activity coefficient would then be, in terms of molalities,*

$$\gamma_c = \frac{a}{n/(1,000 - nw)}$$

whereas the usual way is

$$\gamma = \frac{a}{n/(1,000)}$$

Hence,

$$\gamma = \gamma_c \frac{1,000}{(1,000 - nw)}$$

that is, as n increases (with increase in concentration), the value of the second factor increases progressively. Indeed, it rises to such an extent that it completely overshadows the decrease in the value of the true activity coefficient, γ_c, with increase in concentration and gives rise to an apparent activity coefficient greater than unity.

Relations Between the Various Activity Coefficients

Consider an electrolyte such as $M_x A_y$ which in solution is dissociated to give $xM^{z+} + yA^{z-}$. The activity of the electrolyte as a whole is not the same as those of its respective ions and it is therefore necessary to relate these.

The activity of the electrolyte *as a whole* (a_2) is defined by

$$a_2 = (a_+)^x(a_-)^y \qquad . \qquad . \qquad . \quad (27)$$

Let
$$x + y = v \qquad . \qquad . \qquad . \quad (28)$$

then the (geometric) mean activity of the electrolyte ($a \pm$) is defined by

$$a\pm = \sqrt[v]{a_2} \qquad . \qquad . \qquad . \qquad . \quad (29a)$$

$$= \sqrt[v]{(a_+)^x(a_-)^y} \qquad . \qquad . \qquad . \quad (29b)$$

$$= \sqrt[v]{(m_+\gamma_+)^x(m_-\gamma_-)^y} \qquad . \qquad . \quad (29c)$$

* Concentrations may be stated in terms of molalities or molarities. Accordingly we have either

activity = molar concentration × molar activity coefficient

i.e.

$$a = [\text{Electrolyte}] \times f_{\text{electrolyte}}$$

or

activity = molal concentration × molal activity coefficient,

i.e.

$$a = m \times \gamma$$

$$= \sqrt[y]{(C_+f_+)^x(C_-f_-)^y} \qquad . \qquad . \quad (29d)$$

$$= m_{\pm}\gamma_{\pm} \qquad . \qquad . \qquad . \qquad . \quad (29e)$$

$$= C_{\pm}f_{\pm} \qquad . \qquad . \qquad . \qquad . \quad (29f)$$

where $m_{\pm}$ and $C_{\pm}$ are the (geometric) mean molality and molarity respectively of the electrolyte as a whole, and $\gamma_{\pm}$ and $f_{\pm}$ are the corresponding mean activity coefficients.

TABLE 2

MEAN ACTIVITY COEFFICENTS ($\gamma \pm$) OF VARIOUS ELECTROLYTES IN AQUEOUS
SOLUTION AT 25°C

Mola-lity	0·001	0·005	0·01	0·02	0·05	0·10	0·20	0·50	1·0	2·0
HCl	0·966	0·928	0·905	0·875	0·830	0·796	0·767	0·757	0·809	1·009
NaCl	0·966	0·929	0·904	0·875	0·823	0·778	0·732	0·679	0·656	0·670
NaBr	0·966	0·934	0·914	0·887	0·844	0·800	0·740	0·695	0·686	0·734
KBr	0·965	0·927	0·903	0·872	0·822	0·771	0·721	0·657	0·617	0·596
KCl	0·965	0·927	0·901	—	0·815	0·769	0·717	0·650	0·605	0·575
H_2SO_4	0·830	0·643	0·545	0·455	0·341	0·266	0·210	0·155	0·131	0·125
Na_2SO_4	0·887	0·778	0·714	0·641	0·53	0·45	0·36	0·27	0·20	—
K_2SO_4	0·85	—	0·71	—	0·52	0·43	0·421	—	—	—
$BaCl_2$	—	—	0·723	—	0·559	0·492	0·436	0·390	0·389	—
$Ba(OH)_2$	—	—	0·712	—	0·526	0·443	0·370	—	—	—
$Ca(NO_3)_2$	0·88	—	0·71	—	0·54	0·48	0·42	0·38	0·35	0·35
$CuCl_2$	0·89	—	0·72	—	0·58	0·52	0·47	0·42	0·43	0·51
$MgCl_2$	—	—	—	—	—	0·565	0·520	0·514	0·613	0·143
$ZnCl_2$	0·88	0·789	0·731	0·667	0·628	0·575	0·459	0·394	0·337	0·284
$CaCl_2$	0·888	0·789	0·732	0·669	0·584	0·531	0·482	0·457	0·509	0·807
$CuSO_4$	0·762	0·75	0·404	0·320	0·216	0·150	0·110	0·067	—	—
$MgSO_4$	—	—	0·40	0·32	0·22	0·18	0·13	0·088	0·064	0·055
$LaCl_3$	0·853	0·716	0·637	0·552	0·417	0·356	0·298	0·303	0·387	0·954

For any electrolyte as a whole, the molarity of which is C, we have

$$C_+ = xC \qquad . \qquad . \qquad . \qquad . \quad \text{(30a)}$$

$$C_- = yC \qquad . \qquad . \qquad . \qquad . \quad \text{(30b)}$$

and therefore by (29a)

$$a_\pm = \{(xC)^x(yC)^y\}^{1/\nu}f_\pm \qquad . \qquad . \quad \text{(31a)}$$

$$= \{(x^x y^y)^{1/\nu}\}Cf_\pm \qquad . \qquad . \quad \text{(31b)}$$

Expressing the electrolyte concentration in molalities, we have for an electrolyte the molality of which is 'm'

$$m_+ = xm \quad . \qquad . \qquad . \qquad . \quad \text{(32a)}$$

$$m_- = ym \qquad . \qquad . \qquad . \qquad . \quad \text{(32b)}$$

and therefore by (29a)

$$a_\pm = \{(xm)^x(ym)^y\}^{1/\nu}\gamma_\pm \qquad . \qquad . \quad \text{(33a)}$$

$$= (x^x y^y)^{1/\nu}m\gamma_\pm \qquad . \qquad . \quad \text{(33b)}$$

Considerations Relating to the Applicability of the Comprehensive Solubility Product Equation

INCREASE in the value of the ionic strength of the solvent medium accompanying the addition of electrolytes to a sparingly soluble electrolyte may result in variation in the values of K, a_{H_2O}, a_{solid}, b and c. (See equations (9) and (10), p. 4). Accurate assessment of such possible variations depends on the accuracy with which several factors, on which the above functions depend, are known. Consequently, the following assessment will, perforce, be mainly qualitative.

Variation in the Value of K

The value of the solubility product constant K depends on the nature of the solvent and the solid. Its value is bound to change with variation in the value of the heat of solution on the introduction of co-solutes, since it obeys the general relationship

$$\log K = \frac{-\Delta H}{2 \cdot 303 RT} + C \quad . \quad . \quad . \quad (20)$$

where C is an integration constant.

The effect of the introduction of co-solutes on the heat of solution does not seem to have been determined. However, changes in the heat of solution of single electrolytes with change of quantity dissolved have been determined by Lange and others[73] (for reviews see Lange and Robinson,[74] and Robinson and Wallace[75]) who found that for uni-univalent salts at 25°C, below $I = 0 \cdot 01$, the relation $\Delta H = -280\sqrt{c}$ (where c is the molar concentration) is approached only by highly hydrated electrolytes, e.g., LiF, and that the less hydrated the ions are, the lower the value of the slope. Now, the value of K depends not only on ΔH but also on the magnitude of the integration constant C and, in general, the less hydrated the ion—that is, the lower the ratio $\dfrac{\text{charge}}{\text{surface area}}$* which is directly responsible for the attachment of the water molecules to the charged ions—the smaller is the overall variation in the value of ΔH with ionic strength. Consequently, the lower the ratio $\dfrac{\text{charge}}{\text{surface area}}$ of the constituent ions of both solute and co-solute, the smaller is the variation of K with increase in ionic strength.

Variation in the Value of a_{H_2O}

It has already been pointed out in Chapter 1 that increase in electrolyte concentration, by resulting in an increase in the value of the overall dipole moment of the water molecules, results in two opposing effects so far as the value of the activity of the water is concerned; and that consequently it is difficult to give an accurate assessment of the overall result. Further, there do not appear to be comprehensive or easily interpretable data concerning the values of the dipole moment of water in electrolyte solutions. Qualitatively, this difficulty may be resolved if one accepts the assumption that increase in the value of the dipole moment of water molecules is related to the decrease in vapour pressure with increase in electrolyte concentration. Simple considerations suggest that the above parallelism is reasonable; consequently the variation in dipole moment of water molecules is comparatively small in those ranges

---

* The association of dipole molecules with an ion depends on the magnitude of the charge on the ion, the corresponding (oppositely charged) pole strength, the dielectric and the distance between the two. The direct attraction may be represented by the expression $\dfrac{q \times \delta}{\epsilon \times d^2}$ where q is the charge on the ion, δ is the pole strength, ϵ is the dielectric constant and d is the distance between the centre of the ion and the position of the pole. Opposing this attraction is the repulsive force between the ion and the (further away) similarly charged pole of the dipole. A parallel equation may be written for this repulsive force, allowing for the variation in the dielectric constant and the greater distance. And since the distance over which the repulsive force acts is greater, the overall effect is attraction between the ion and the dipole as oriented. For a given dipole-molecule, the greater the ionic charge and the smaller the ionic radius, the greater is the overall attraction. Hence, the greater the ratio charge/(radius)^2, the greater is the overall attraction, and therefore the greater is the number of water molecules attached to the ion. The above overall attraction may be formulated in terms of the field strength at the periphery of the anhydrous ion. The greater the field strength—which can be represented by charge/(surface area)—the greater is the attractive force. The two expressions, namely, charge/(radius)^2 and charge/(surface area), are directly related since (surface area) $\propto$ (radius)^2.

of electrolyte concentration where the aqueous vapour pressure variation from that of pure water is comparatively small. And further since increase in the dipole moment value gives rise to opposing effects, small variations in aqueous vapour pressure may be taken to represent still smaller changes in a_{H_2O} involved in the comprehensive solubility product equation.

The lowering of aqueous vapour pressure in solutions up to $I = 0.01$ is comparatively small. Thus, at $20°C$, it may be inferred from graphs drawn from available data in the International Critical Tables[76] that a solution of $0.01M$ NaCl has a vapour pressure of 17.49 mm of mercury, while that of pure water is 17.54 mm of mercury at the same temperature, that is, the aqueous vapour pressure in a $0.01M$ NaCl solution is about 99.7 per cent of that in pure water. In general, the higher the number of water molecules with which the electrolyte is associated, the greater is the reduction in the value of the aqueous vapour pressure, and hence the higher is the value of the dipole moment and the greater is likely to be the variation of a_{H_2O} from that in very dilute solutions. For uni-univalent electrolytes, up to $I = 0.01$, the variation in a_{H_2O} is likely to be smaller than the above 0.3 per cent. However, for higher valency electrolytes the reduction in a_{H_2O} is likely to be greater, since their ratio of charge/(surface area), and consequently the dipole moment of the water, is likely to be far greater than that of pure water.

Variation in the Numerical Values of the Number of Associated Water Molecules b and c

Since the activity of the water has to be raised to the power of $(xb + yc)$, the greater the values of b and c—that is, the greater the numbers of the water molecules associated with the respective ions— the greater *exponentially* is the effect of the reduced activity of the water. Let $(b + c) = 10$ when $x = y = 1$, then the ratio

$$\frac{(a_{H_2O})_{I=0.01}^{10}}{(a_{H_2O})_{I \to 0}^{10}} \lesssim 97.3 \text{ per cent} \qquad \text{(using the previous values for vapour pressures)}$$

The higher the values of b and c the greater is the effect, and, of course, the higher the ratio charge/(surface area) the more pronounced will be the effect.

The above considerations hold provided there are sufficient *free* solvent water molecules present to satisfy the water association requirements of both original and co-solute. In concentrated solutions of electrolytes this proportionality is likely to be affected by the shortage of free water molecules and the resulting competition between the two electrolytes for them. Equilibrium (B) (see p. 3) and the corresponding comprehensive solubility product equation (9) can no longer be considered accurate and must be replaced by the equilibrium—

$$M_x^{z+}A_y^{z-} + \frac{F^{z'+}}{E^{z'-}} \cdot dH_2O \rightleftharpoons \frac{x(M^{z+} \cdot b'H_2O)}{y(A^{z-} \cdot c'H_2O)} + \frac{F^{z'+}}{E^{z'-}} \cdot (d - b' - c')H_2O \quad (G)$$

where FE is the added co-solute, d is the number of water molecules with which it would be associated—if free to do so—the factors z^+, z^-, z'^+ and z'^- represent the respective charges, b' and c' are the reduced numbers of water molecules associated with the original electrolyte as a result of the competition for water molecules.

Variation in the Value of a_{solid}

It has already been stressed in this book that the activity of a solid can be altered by changes in surface tension values. For a concise evaluation of changes in a_{solid} it is necessary to know the corresponding values of the surface tension between the solid and the surrounding solution and not the surface tension between the surrounding solution and air; the two may differ considerably. Unfortunately, data concerning the variation of the surface tension of interfacial solid-solutions with electrolyte concentration are, apparently, not available. In the absence of these, the approximation that the variations in the value of the interfacial solid-solution surface tension with electrolyte concentration run parallel to those of solution-air interfacial surface tensions is not unreasonable, and we shall use this likely parallelism to obtain information on which to base an assessment of the variation of a_{solid} with electrolyte concentration.

Over the approximate range of $I = 0.0$ to $I = 0.01$, for inorganic electrolytes, the solution-air interfacial surface tension changes are indeed small. Thus, a 0.025M solution of NaCl in water shows only a 0.1 per cent increase in surface tension, compared with that of pure water. However, over higher ionic strength ranges, the surface tension variation may become considerable, and there a_{solid} may vary appreciably from that in very dilute solutions. Additionally, a normally hydrated solid may be dehydrated when in contact with concentrated solutions of other electrolytes.

Returning now to the overall value of the product

$$\{K(a_{H_2O})^{(xb+yc)}a_{\text{solid}}\}$$

it can be seen that provided

(i) the deviation of K, from its value in *very* dilute solutions, is slight,

(ii) the reduction in the value of the vapour pressure is slight,

(iii) the numerical value of $(xb + yc)$ is small, and

(iv) the addition of co-solutes hardly alters the surface tension, then the above product is only slightly altered.

Now, as has already been pointed out, for uni-univalent electrolyte co-solutes in concentration up to approximately $0.01I$, requirement (ii) is practically fulfilled, while requirement (iii) is also met by solute and co-solute having a low value of $(x + y)$, the limiting factor being 2, and whose association with water molecules $(b + c)$ is small, i.e. ions having comparatively large radii, and whose charges are as low as possible; the latter requirement tending also to fulfil requirement (i). Also requirement (iv) is generally met over this region of ionic strength. Hence, in such cases the left-hand-side product in equation (10) is constant and we obtain the reduced activity solubility product equation (5) (*see* page 2).

In this connexion it is pertinent to consider the work of Brønsted and LaMer[9] who set out to test the application of the Debye-Hückel theory[10] to the solubility of sparingly soluble electrolytes using the equation

$$\log (S/S_o) = Az^+z^-(\sqrt{I} - \sqrt{I_o}) \qquad . \qquad . \qquad (34)$$

where S and S_o refer to the solubilities in the respective presence and absence of the co-solute, I and I_o refer to the corresponding ionic strengths, and A is a constant. (This equation is a direct result of the Debye-Hückel limiting equation (16).) The equation (34) is based on the assumption that equilibrium (A) and equation (5) were correct. Brønsted and LaMer obtained for the range up to $I = 0.01$ results which are in good agreement with Debye-Hückel's calculated values for the activity coefficients, particularly of $1:1$ electrolytes, thus proving, incidentally, the constancy of the thermodynamic solubility product over that region. At first sight this agreement suggests that the equilibrium equation (A), which the literature generally adopts, is intrinsically correct and that equilibrium (B) and equation (10) are unnecessary complications. However, if we investigate the experimental conditions and materials of Brønsted and LaMer we find that such an interpretation is short-sighted and that the reason for the constancy of the reduced activity solubility product equation in their case was merely due to the previously stated requirements having been met unwittingly in their work. These authors used original solutes having large ionic radii such as those belonging to the following—

$[Co(NH_3)_4(NO_2)(CNS)][Co(NH_3)_2(NO_2)_2(C_2O_4)]$ 1:1 valency

$[Co(NH_3)_4(C_2O_4)]_2[S_2O_6]$ 1:2 valency

$[Co(NH_3)_6][Co(NH_3)_2(NO_2)_2(C_2O_4)]_3$ 3:1 valency

for which b and c are likely to be very small. Also they noted that when both ions of the saturating salt have high valencies discrepancies were found which became more pronounced as the concentrations of these co-solute ions increased. The latter osbervations are, of course, in line with requirements (i), (ii) and (iii) in agreement with the above considerations.

However, in the absence of the comprehensive solubility product equation, these deviations have been generally attributed to deviations of the activity coefficients of the solute ions from the values assigned to them by the Debye-Hückel theory and its limiting equation— that is, to variations in the activity of the solute only. But neglect of the functions of K, a_{H_2O}, a_{solid} and b and c cannot be considered reasonable in solutions having ionic strengths greater than $I = 0.01$ in the case of low valency ions, and even below this value when higher valency ions are used. Consequently, the results of Brønsted and LaMer, instead of being considered contradictory to the comprehensive activity solubility product concept, rather indicate the correctness of the comprehensive approach.

APPENDIX 7

Solubility Product Values

THE term Solubility Product, as referred to in the literature, is a numerical value which strictly speaking is the product of the activities of the respective ions of the specified electrolyte in its saturated solution. For electrolytes having solubility product values equivalent to solubilities below 10^{-4}M the ionic concentrations are practically equal to the corresponding activities (within 1 per cent error) and therefore the concentration and activity solubility products are practically the same.

The solubility product values available have been determined by a variety of methods, the major ones of which are those based on electromotive-force measurements, conductivity determinations and solubility evaluations; osmotic pressure and depression of freezing point methods were also used. The first method can be considered to give the activity solubility product—that is, the product of the activities of the "free" ionic species concerned, not taking into account the hydrated ionic pairs—while determinations of solubility give an overall result which allows for the presence of both hydrated (and any anhydrous) covalent molecules and hydrated ion-pairs; as such it does not give a true value of the solubility product unless the requisite allowances are made. Hydrated ion-pairs, on the whole, do not contribute to the conductivity of the solution, as they do not tend to move towards either electrode, and in very dilute solutions they are unable to affect the dielectric constant of the medium to such an extent that it in turn will affect the conductivity of the solution as a whole. Hence, the results of conductivity measurements, when translated in terms of solubility product values, should give an activity solubility product. In general it would be correct to conclude that, unless the concentration of the covalent and hydrated ion-pairs are small indeed or can be allowed for, the

76

solubility product value determined by electrometric methods will not be in agreement with that deduced from solubility evaluations. Further, the solubility product is an equilibrium constant, and one cannot be certain whether the solubility product value stated was determined under equilibrium conditions in every single case published.

Since the process of solution of a solid is accompanied by heat change, the solubility product value of a given solid may vary by several hundred per cent over a temperature range of 10°C. Now, "room temperature" may vary from 15°C in winter to 25°C in summer, if not more. Consequently, it is not very accurate, to say the least, to give solubility product values for "laboratory temperature," as some text books give, to within the second or even the first decimal.

There are considerable data concerning solubility product values to be found scattered in the literature. Many can be found or deduced from data in the *International Critical Tables* and *Solubility of Inorganic Substances* (by Seidell). But the most comprehensive, including up-to-date, source of information now is the publication by the Chemical Society (London) of *Stability Constants, Part II, Inorganic Ligands*, 1958. This publication has brought all published solubility product data, whether evaluated experimentally or theoretically, within a single volume. Perusal of this book will show considerable variation in solubility product values for some specified substances at a specified temperature between the results obtained by different investigators.*

Sometimes the differences may be attributed to the existence of different solid forms of the same substance, e.g. the existence of the sphalerite and wurtzite forms of zinc sulphide, but sometimes they may be due to the solids being at different stages on the way to equilibrium when the measurements were taken.

The considerable variation may be illustrated on consideration of the following data available on use of free energy considerations (associated with electrometric methods) for zinc sulphide and lead sulphide, at 25°C at ionic strength approaching zero.

α-ZnS	β-ZnS		"Zinc Sulphide"		
log S.P. $-24\cdot10$;	$-25\cdot15$ $-22\cdot80$	$-21\cdot6$;	$-22\cdot2$;	$-23\cdot8$;	$-26\cdot13$

Lead Sulphide

log S.P. $-27\cdot10$;	$-28\cdot15$;	$-28\cdot17$;	$-29\cdot15$

On the other hand, good agreement has been obtained in some other

---

* Differences equivalent to as high as 10^3 to 10^4 per cent have been noted. Variations of this order are too large to be attributable to "experimental error."

cases, such as that of silver chloride at 25°C and $I \to 0$ using potentiometric measurements.

Silver Chloride

log S.P. −9·74;   −9·76;   −9·71;   −9·749

and using conductivity measurements also at 25°C and for $I \to 0$

log S.P. −9·77;   −9·74;   −9·75

The effect of temperature on the solubility product value can be accurately demonstrated only in those cases where there is hardly any variation in the experimental value for a single temperature. For this reason, this effect can be readily demonstrated in the case of silver chloride, thus, using conductivity measurements. The following data have been recorded by Owen[80] and Owen and Brinkley.[81]

Temperature	5°C	15°C	25°C	35°C	45°C
log S.P. (at $I \to 0$)	− 10·595	− 10·152	− 9·749	− 9·381	− 9·043

The heat of reaction has been calculated to vary from 16·02 kcal at 15°C to 15·31 kcal at 35°C.

The above data are merely illustrative of the possible agreements or variations to be found in the literature. For a comprehensive reference to the numerous data available in the literature it is advisable to consult the above-quoted book on stability constants.

The Teaching and Study of the Solubility Product Principle

THE uses of the orthodox solubility product principle are limited because the ranges over which its reduced equations apply accurately are relatively small. Further, its effectiveness over the range covered by the comprehensive equation is, quantitatively, considerably narrowed because of the difficulty involved in accurate assessment of the variation of the factors of solid activity, number of associated molecules of and activity of water. Even the constancy of the thermodynamic equilibrium "constant," may be called into question because sufficient rise in electrolyte concentration is bound to lead to pronounced and fundamental changes in the medium to such an extent that its final properties may represent practically a different medium from that of the original water solvent which contained only very small ionic concentrations. Because of this, some may be tempted to teach or accept the solubility product principle as a "Law" which is, however, highly approximate and to jettison any inconvenient "exceptions." Such an attitude cannot be defended on scientific grounds, even though it may be considered expedient. The scientific perspective requires a thorough examination of the basis and limitations of any generalization. It is most unfortunate that this approach is not emphasized in some schools—in which many future scientists obtain their introduction to scientific knowledge and supposed outlook. The present fashion of preparing for examinations tends to encourage a non-scientific attitude in both teachers and students of scientific subjects. It is hoped that the presentation, in this book, of the true solubility product principle will encourage a scientific assessment of the principle rather than blind repetition in attempting its application to problems involved in chemical analysis.

A hurdle often encountered by teachers or students of physical chemistry in the process of imparting or absorbing its principles is the difficulty in forming concepts of what is happening. But in this instance the concept of precipitation or dissolving of a substance is easily visualized by the student. Because this picture is clear, it is possible to weave around it various related physico-chemical principles and therefore present an overall picture of their applicabilities. Thus the study of the background of the solubility product principle permits correlation of the thermodynamic and kinetic theoretical tools, the concept of dipole moments, activity coefficients, partial ionization, solid solution and water transport (see later). The limitations of the applicability of the solubility product equations should not be considered a nuisance; rather the reverse. These limitations should be used to illustrate the various other physico-chemical principles and compromises which one encounters in the scientific field.

In teaching a scientific generalization, the impression may be given that the more strictly one applies a set of conditions, the more accurate is the generalization, *ad infinitum*. The teaching of the solubility product principle may well be used to show the limitations of the above generalization. Thus, it is correct to say that the more dilute the solution the greater the degree of accuracy obtained on application of the solubility product principle to a sparingly soluble electrolyte. However, as the solubility product value becomes very small indeed, other considerations affect its applicability. For example, thermodynamic considerations, on which the solubility product principle depends, require a minimum number of molecules to apply with accuracy. Yet the solubility product values are sometimes below the minimum requirements of thermodynamic rules. Thus, the solubility product value of mercuric sulphide is about 10^{-50}. This means that, assuming complete ionization, 10^{-25} gramme ions of Hg^{++} and 10^{-25} gramme ions of $S^=$ are present per litre. Now, the value of the Avogadro Number is $6 \cdot 03 \times 10^{23}$ molecules per gramme molecule. This means that there are about $(6 \times 10^{23} \times 10^{-25})$ i.e. $\approx 6 \times 10^{-2}$ molecules, each, of Hg^{++} and $S^=$ per litre, or one ion-molecule, each, of Hg^{++} and $S^=$ in 17 litres. By no stretch of imagination could thermodynamic principles be strictly applicable to such small numbers. It is perhaps questionable whether a solubility product of the order of 10^{-28}, as in the case of bi-valent sulphides such as cadmium sulphide, is equivalent to $\approx (6 \times 10^{23} \times 10^{-14})$, i.e. $\approx 6 \times 10^9$ ion-molecules each of Cd^{++} and $S^=$, assuming complete ionization (which is itself unlikely) is within the minimum requirements of thermodynamics.

In this connexion it is interesting to consider the limitations of the solubility product principle, as the value of the solubility product becomes very small indeed, from the kinetic standpoint. For precipitation to take place, it is essential that oppositely charged ions collide with one another. The *limiting* case is that in which every collision is effective so far as dehydration of the hydrated ions and eventual precipitation is concerned.* Now, according to the kinetic theory, $Z = \sqrt{2}\pi\rho^2 \bar{c}n^2$, where $\rho =$ the molecular diameter, $n =$ the number of molecules per c.c., and $\bar{c} =$ the root mean square velocity at the given temperature. Using this equation we can calculate—very approximately, but to an extent sufficient to demonstate the point under consideration—the number of collisions in solution per c.c. per sec on the assumption that it is approximately the same as the corresponding one in the gaseous state.† Applying this approach to the precipitation of HgS, using the previous number of ion-molecules per litre (and converting it into molecules per c.c.), assuming $\bar{c} \cong 180$ m/sec, $\rho \cong 10^{-7}$ cm, we have

$$z \cong \sqrt{2}\,\pi(10^{-7})^2\,\frac{cm^2}{molecules^2} \times 18,000\,\frac{cm}{sec}$$

$$\times\,(12 \times 10^{-2} \times 10^{-3})^2\,\frac{molecules^2}{(cm^3)^2}$$

i.e. $z \cong 10^{-17}$ collisions per c.c. per sec. In other words 10^{+17} seconds will pass before a single collision will take place at all—in a solution having concentrations of Hg^{++} and $S^=$ equal to, or just greater than, those required by the solubility product of HgS; this value includes "ineffective" collisions between similarly charged

---

* The velocity of chemical reaction is covered by the Law of Mass Action, and in the case of a binary reaction between two substances, say A and B, we have

$$v = k[A][B]$$

The value of the velocity constant, k, in the case of simple reactions depends on the energy of activation and generally obeys the relation $k = PZe^{-E/RT}$, where P is a probability factor, Z is the number of collisions per second per c.c., E is the energy of activation, R is the gas constant per mole and T is the absolute temperature. Now, in most ionic reactions leading to precipitation the energy of activation which is essentially the energy of dehydration of the ions, e.g. in the case of AgCl formation,

$$(Ag\cdot bH_2O)^+ + (Cl\cdot cH_2O)^- = \overset{+\ -}{AgCl} + (b + c)H_2O$$

is comparatively small and therefore many, or most of the collisions result in dehydration followed by precipitation if nuclei are present. Consequently, in such simple cases we can take as our guiding principle that nearly every collision is effective.

† This assumption is not unreasonable because molecules in solution appear to obey gaseous laws. Thus, the osmotic pressure of a solution is given by the Ideal Gas Equation $PV = nRT$ which indicates that the molecules of solute behave like a gas in solution.

ions and it assumes the presence of a nucleus. Thus the solubility product value, when extremely small, cannot be taken as a criterion of the ionic product actually required for precipitation to take place.

So far we have considered the dissolving of electrolytes into, and their removal from, solution in terms of entry into or exit from the solution on the basis of the solubility product principle. However, an overall bird's-eye view encompassing a far wider field can be obtained by regarding these reactions in terms of a general theory of water transfer which applies particularly well to the precipitations of comparatively soluble electrolytes on addition of other soluble electrolytes, e.g. the precipitation of NaCl on HCl addition.

Consider the following series of processes. A solution of ether in water is prepared. The addition of NaCl to saturation value results in the ether being salted out. The introduction of HCl results in precipitation of the NaCl. Addition of concentrated sulphuric acid, to the liquid medium, results in combination of the water with the former and the consequent expulsion of HCl. Finally, the addition of solid P_2O_5 to the "diluted" sulphuric acid results in the water being transferred to and combining with the phosphorus pentoxide to give H_3PO_4, the sulphuric acid having then been liberated. These series of processes can be represented as—

$$H_2O$$
$$\downarrow \ + \text{ether}$$
$$H_2O \ \ldots\ldots\ldots \text{ether solution}$$
$$\downarrow \ + \text{solid NaCl}$$
$$H_2O \ \ldots\ \text{NaCl solution} + \text{ether}$$
$$\downarrow \ + \text{HCl}$$
$$H_2O \ \ldots\ \text{HCl solution} + \text{NaCl}$$
$$\downarrow \ + \text{conc. } H_2SO_4$$
$$H_2O \ \ldots\ H_2SO_4 \text{ compound} + \text{HCl}$$
$$\downarrow \ + P_2O_5$$
$$H_3PO_4 + H_2SO_4$$

Precipitation and dissolution of sparingly soluble electrolytes from their solutions on addition of other electrolytes form but a small fraction of the field of precipitations and solutions encountered in the overall field of electrolyte precipitations and solutions; and this latter field, in turn, forms a small portion of the overall field of solvent transfer. If the usual solubility product treatment is followed and the precipitations and solutions of sparingly soluble electrolytes be still written in terms of equilibria neglecting interaction with the solvent, then the picture presented will be inadequate, and the opportunity will have been missed of illustrating the correlation of several physico-chemical theories.

One further point deserves particular consideration, namely that of partial ionization. Partial ionization has, in the past, been usually treated in terms of the Law of Mass Action, but without inclusion of water of hydration. The picture usually drawn assumed a solid substance, represented as a covalent compound, in equilibrium with its saturated solution which contained covalent molecules in equilibrium with the ionic forms. Considering a solid such as M_xA_y in equilibrium with its saturated solution, the usual representation has been

$$M_xA_y \rightleftharpoons M_xA_y \rightleftharpoons xM^{z+} + yA^{z-}$$

solid   covalent   ions
molecules

solution

Historically we may trace the origin of such representations. Originally a saturated solution of a strong electrolyte such as sodium chloride in equilibrium with its solid was represented by the scheme

$$NaCl \rightleftharpoons NaCl \rightleftharpoons Na^+ + Cl^-$$

solid   covalent   ions
molecule

solution

This representation did not withstand the accumulation of scientific knowledge, e.g. the X-ray evidence, that sodium chloride is completely ionized in the solid state, and the redrawn picture was represented as

$$\overset{+}{N}a\overset{-}{Cl} \rightleftharpoons \overset{+}{N}a\overset{-}{Cl} \rightleftharpoons Na^+ + Cl^-$$

solid   ion pairs   separate ions
electrolyte

solution

Any experimentally determined deviation from the prediction of the Law of Mass Action, e.g. by electrometric methods, was assumed to be due to variation in activity coefficient values. However, in the case of weak electrolytes the previous picture—involving equilibrium distribution of anhydrous covalent molecules and anhydrous ions—was maintained. Now the process of solution of the solid depends on absorption of the energy change involved in the process of hydration. Hence, the solute "molecules" present in solution should be mainly, if not wholly, in a hydrated state, and the concentration of anhydrous covalent solute units in solution should be comparatively negligible. It follows that the significant degrees of partial ionization noted in the case of weak electrolytes—which cannot be attributed solely to variation in activity coefficient values—cannot reasonably be described in terms of the existence of anhydrous units such as anhydrous covalent molecules and anhydrous ion pairs. It is more reasonable to represent the solubilities of weak electrolytes such as zinc sulphide, in terms of the following equilibrium which allows for a high dipolarity of the molecule as a whole

In the above representation the solid ZnS is considered a covalent compound possessing a dipole moment. Some might prefer to write the above as an electrolyte solid having highly polarized ions, instead of a covalent compound having a high dipole moment. At extreme ends of the scale a clear distinction could be made between the two types of representation, but in some intermediate cases it would be difficult to assign one particular structure with certainty. However, when it is considered preferable to consider the solid substance in terms of an ionized solid electrolyte having highly polarized ions, the representation can be as follows*—

The Significance and Estimation of Activity Coefficient Values

The activity coefficient values given in the tables as determined experimentally are the geometric mean activity coefficients of the respective electrolytes. The term "mean activity coefficient of an electrolyte" may lead to misunderstanding unless its definition is clearly appreciated. It really refers to the *ions* of the electrolyte and is a geometrically averaged activity coefficient. This is so because there are no exact thermodynamic methods available for evaluating the true activity coefficient of a given ion. To understand the significance of the mean activity coefficient, consider the following

* This representation is incomplete, because several other associations are possible and because the correct picture is three-dimensional and not two-dimensional.

case. The mean activity coefficient of the electrolyte HCl in its 0·1M solution is given in the table as 0·796, i.e. $f_\pm = 0·796$. It means that in this solution—in which HCl is generally considered to be completely ionized, i.e. [H$^+$] = 0·1 and Cl$^-$ = 0·1—the product $(f_{H^+})(f_{Cl^-})$ is experimentally evaluated as 0·6336; and since one cannot thermodynamically evaluate from this the individual values of f_{H^+} and f_{Cl^-}, one writes $(f_\pm)^2 = 0·6336$. Therefore $f_\pm = \sqrt[2]{0·6336} = 0·796$. So long as we use this activity coefficient in calculations involving HCl as a whole, no problem arises since $(f_\pm)^2 = (f_{H^+})(f_{Cl^-})$. However, when we require knowledge of the value of f_{H^+} when another ionic equilibrium, or electrolyte, containing H$^+$ is involved, difficulties arise.

Consider the case of H$_2$S dissolved in a 0·1M HCl solution. The question naturally arises whether the activity coefficients of the H$^+$ and Cl$^-$ (and therefore also their mean activity coefficient) retain their original value in absence of H$_2$S. The answer is in the affirmative, because the ionic strength of the HCl solution is unaffected by introduction of the un-ionized H$_2$S and because the concentrations of the H$^+$, HS$^-$ and S$^=$ ions derived from the ionization of the H$_2$S are minute compared with those derived from the HCl. Now, in the H$_2$S ionization we have, writing the overall equilibrium as H$_2$S $\rightleftharpoons$ 2H$^+$ + S$^=$,

$$\frac{(a_{H^+})^2(a_{S^-})}{a_{H_2S}} = K$$

We can substitute [H$_2$S] for a_{H_2S} because the activity coefficients of non-electrolytes, in dilute solutions, are almost equal to unity. Since [H$_2$S] is known to be equal to 0·1M, we have

$$(a_{H^+})^2(a_{S^=}) = 0·1K, \text{ or } [H^+]^2(f_{H^+})^2(a_{S^-}) = 0·1K$$

The value of K is known. The value of the [H$^+$], fixed by the overriding HCl concentration, is 0·1, and if we can assess the value of f_{H^+}, then $a_{S^=}$ can be evaluated. Now, as pointed out above, the exact value of f_{H^+} is unknown. The question naturally arises; what methods can one adopt for the evaluation of f_{H^+}, and how accurate can they be?

The following are possible—

(a) THE SUBSTITUTION OF $(f_\pm)_{HCl}$ FOR (f_{H^+})

This method may be considered expedient in that the inclusion of activity coefficients represents a nearer approximation towards the correct value, but nevertheless may involve a high degree of inaccuracy, since (f_{H^+}) cannot be exactly equal to $(f_\pm)_{HCl}$ because while the charges of the H^+ and Cl^- are of the same magnitude, their ionic diameters are different. These differences result in different electric field strengths at the surfaces of the two ions and therefore in different activities. Only when both these factors are equal, can the two ions have the same activity. This is practically so in the case of KCl. Then

$$(f_{K^+}) \cong (f_{Cl^-}) \cong (f_\pm)_{KCl}$$

The degree of inaccuracy involved in this method depends then on the difference between (f_{H^+}) and $(f_\pm)_{electrolyte}$ and on the power to which the mean activity coefficient has to be raised. Its use appears permissible—sometimes it is the only method—where the degree of uncertainty is already large and where a somewhat nearer approximation towards the correct value is desired—for example, the calculation on p. 46 where ratios > 250 have been noted. But it is always necessary to bear in mind the limitations of such a substitution. This limitation applies when pH values are considered. Sörensen[87,88] originally defined the pH scale as $pH = \log \dfrac{1}{[H^+]}$ and therefore equal to $- \log [H^+]$. The more accurate, modern, definition is $pH = - \log (a_{H^+}) = - \log [H^+](f_{H^+})$. Now, in practice the value of $(f_\pm)$ is substituted for (f_{H^+}), because $(a_\pm)_{acid}$ is substituted for (a_{H^+}). Hence, the exact significance of the pH values quoted is open to discussion[89,90].

(b) Substitution of $(f_\pm)$ Values of Other Electrolytes

Substitution of $(f_\pm)$ values of other electrolytes having the same type of charge-ion distribution as that of $S^=$ and H^+ ions under identical ionic strength conditions may be used. This method has been adopted in Example 2 (see later).

Either method is open to criticism. However, in the absence of more reliable, or any, data covering the activity coefficients of individual ions, such substitutions represent nearer approximations towards the real state of affairs.

Examples and Problems

THERE are large numbers of different categories and conditions of solubilities and precipitations to be found in chemical analysis. It is not possible, or necessary, to work out examples connected with the various possibilities. In any assessment or calculation of the final result it is, unfortunately, necessary to make some assumptions because of insufficient data, insufficiently defined conditions under which the data were obtained or approximations and assumptions made in the original derivation and calculation of the particular constants. For these reasons the following assessments and calculations are approximate. The purpose of these assessments is not to achieve absolutely correct results, but rather to illustrate the influence of side-effects on the final results.

Example 1

0·0585 g of NaCl are added to 1 litre of a saturated solution of AgCl at 25°C when the activity solubility product is $1·78 \times 10^{-10}$. Assess the resulting concentration of silver chloride when equilibrium has been attained.

ASSESSMENT

General. Up to ionic strengths of $\sim I = 0·01$, the ionic activity solubility product of the saturated solution, $(a_{Ag^+})(a_{Cl^-})$, may be considered practically equal to the comprehensive activity solubility product. Hence $[Ag^+][Cl^-](f_{\pm})^2 \cong 1·78 \times 10^{-10}$.

Now, "silver chloride" usually represents the compound AgCl which in its pure saturated solution is generally considered to be practically completely ionized and $[Ag^+] = [AgCl] = [silver\ chloride]$ in solution. However, it is known that solid AgCl, in equilibrium with its saturated solution, dissolves to an increasing extent on progressive rise in the chloride ion content of the solution, as the experimental results of Forbes and Cole[83] have shown. It is clear from their data that the common ion effect is operative pronouncedly in decreasing the solubility of silver chloride up to 0·004N NaCl, but thereafter the solubility increases.

It is therefore necessary to take into consideration the equation $Ag^+ + 2Cl^- \rightleftharpoons AgCl_2^-$. The equilibrium constant for this reaction has been given as $\beta_2 = 5.66$ at $25°C$ for the concentration equilibrium, in dilute solutions, i.e.

$$\frac{[AgCl_2^-]}{[Ag^+][Cl^-]^2} = 5.66*$$

Hence,

$$[AgCl_2^-] = 5.66[Ag^+][Cl^-]^2$$

Now,

$$[\text{Silver chloride}] = [AgCl] + [AgCl_2^-]$$
$$= [Ag^+] + 5.66[Ag^+][Cl^-]^2$$
$$= [Ag^+]\{1 + 5.66[Cl^-]^2\}$$

Evaluation of Chloride Concentration. The chloride content at equilibrium is

$$[\text{Chloride}] = [NaCl] + [AgCl] + 2[AgCl_2 \cdot Na]$$

As the silver concentration is very small compared to the NaCl concentration we have†

$$[NaCl] \gg \{[AgCl] + 2[AgCl_2 \cdot Na]\}$$

and therefore $[Cl^-] \cong \dfrac{0.0585 \text{ g}}{58.5 \text{ g/g equiv.}} = 0.001$ g equiv./litre

Evaluation of $(f_\pm)$. The total ionic strength in solution is made up of the various ionic constituents in solution. Accepting Lewis and Randall's activity coefficient generalization in this very small ionic strength region ($I \cong 0.001$, since NaCl is a uni-univalent electrolyte) we can calculate[17] that $(f_\pm) \cong 0.9$ and $(f_\pm)^2 \cong 0.81$. Therefore,

$$[Ag^+] \cong \frac{1.78 \times 10^{-10}}{(f_\pm)^2[Cl^-]} \cong \frac{1.78 \times 10^{-10}}{0.81 \times 10^{-3}} \cong 2.2 \times 10^{-7}$$

Hence,

$$[\text{Silver chloride}] \cong 2.2 \times 10^{-7}\{1 + 5.66 \times (10^{-3})^2\}$$
$$\cong 2.2 \times 10^{-7}$$

* The equilibrium constant is given in *Stability Constants* as a concentration equilibrium constant for dilute solutions. It is therefore an approximate equilibrium constant and its value will not be the same at $I = 0$.
† The solubility of AgCl in absence of other salts is about 10^{-5}M. The initial concentration of NaCl is 10^{-3}M—that is, over 100 times as large as that of that of AgCl particularly because the common ion effect has reduced the solubility of silver chloride to lower values.

The same numerical result would have been attained, under the given conditions had the [AgCl$_2^-$] been neglected initially. This is due to the low [NaCl] employed and because of the comparatively low value of β_2. In presence of higher NaCl concentrations the effect of the presence of AgCl$_2^-$ would have been pronounced.

General Note. Variations in the numerical value of an equilibrium constant, referring to specific cases, are often found in the literature. When the "constant" refers to "dilute" solutions it is quite likely that the variations are due to evaluations at different ionic strengths associated with neglect of activities. Such variations, assuming that true equilibrium conditions have been attained, are often quite large, and even in meticulous investigations may vary by over $\pm$ 10 per cent owing to the above neglect. Obviously there is no point in including activity coefficient values in equilibrium constant equations which are said to be developed in terms of "dilute" concentrations, because this will not lead to a higher degree of accuracy.

Example 2

Assess the concentration of the sulphide ion in a 0·1M HCl solution saturated with H$_2$S at 25°C. Assume [H$_2$S] to be 0·1M.

ASSESSMENT

The equilibria present in hydrogen sulphide solutions may be represented in terms of the two respective association-dissociations

$$\left.\begin{array}{ll} H^+ + S^= \rightleftharpoons HS^- & K_1 = 8\cdot3 \times 10^{14*} \\ H^+ + HS^- \rightleftharpoons H_2S & K_2 = 1\cdot1 \times 10^7 \end{array}\right\} \text{ for } I \rightrightarrows 0$$

For the overall dissociation we may write

$$S^= + 2H^+ = H_2S, \text{ and } K_3 = K_1 \times K_2 = 9\cdot1 \times 10^{21}\dagger$$

Hence for the overall equilibrium we have

$$\frac{(a_{H_2S})}{(a_{S^=})(a_{H^+})^2} = \frac{[H_2S](f_{H_2S})}{[S^=][H^+]^2(f_{S^=})(f_{H^+})^2} = K_3$$

---

* This value is based on Bruner and Zawadski's[56] and Thiel and Gessner's[85] results. However, considerably different values (also for $I \rightrightarrows 0$, at 25°C) have also been recorded, e.g., 8·3 × 10^{12} according to Goates, Gordon and Faux.[86] See also *Stability Constants*, p. 69.

$\dagger$
$$K_1 = \frac{(a_{HS^-})}{(a_{H^+})(a_{S^=})} \; ; \; K_2 = \frac{(a_{H_2S})}{(a_{H^+})(a_{HS^-})}$$

Therefore,

$$K_1 \times K_2 = \frac{(a_{HS^-})(a_{H_2S})}{(a_{H^+})(a_{S^=})(a_{H^+})(a_{HS^-})} = \frac{(a_{H_2S})}{(a_{H^+})^2(a_{S^=})} = K_3$$

Now, the activity coefficient of an *ion* cannot be determined *experimentally*. What is determined is the mean activity coefficient of the electrolyte species, namely ($f_\pm$). Consequently,

$$K_3 = \frac{[H_2S](f_{H_2S})^*}{[S^=][H^+]^2(f_\pm)^3}$$

Approximations. The activity of a non-electrolyte is hardly affected by the addition of electrolytes, provided both are dilute. In such cases it is reasonable to adopt the convention that the activity of the non-electrolyte is unity and therefore (f_{H_2S}) = 1. Also, since the dissociation of H_2S when alone in solution, is minute and since it is depressed further in the presence of HCl, for the purpose of assessing concentrations the H^+ ions may be considered to be exclusively supplied by the HCl. Hence, $[H^+] = 0.1$.

The computation of the value of ($f_\pm$) requires, however, some consideration. Its value could be assumed to be equal to that of the mean activity coefficient of HCl in its $0.1M$ solution. A similar assessment to this was followed in the calculation on p. 45. Here we shall follow the method whereby the ($f_\pm$) of the electrolytes having the same valency type of ion-charge distribution as that of the $S^=$ and H^+ ions under identical ionic strength conditions, is assumed to have the same value for that involving the $S^=$ and H^+ equilibrium with H_2S.

The ionic strength, supplied by the HCl, is 0.1. Consequently, to assess the approximate value of the mean activity coefficient of the ($2H^+$, $S^=$) electrolyte species in a solution of overall ionic strength of $I = 0.1$ we have to consider and compare the mean activity coefficients of uni-bivalent electrolytes in $I = 0.1$. Now, the activity coefficient values of uni-bivalent electrolytes having divalent negatively-charged monatomic ions, such as $S^=$, have yet been measured. However, the activity coefficient values of other uni-bivalent electrolytes such as K_2SO_4, Na_2SO_4, $CaCl_2$, $BaCl_2$, $ZnCl_2$ and $CuCl_2$ have been determined. Now, from the standpoint of electrical forces it does not matter much, when uni-bivalent electrolytes are considered, whether one deals with electrolytes which are composed of a bivalent negatively charged ion accompanied by two positively charged univalent ions, or a bivalent positively charged ion accompanied by two singly charged negative ions. The ratio of charge/(surface area) is far more important. On this basis, the mean activity coefficients of the above chlorides are more likely to approximate to the mean activity coefficient required than those having large

* See definition of activity coefficients and their relations in Appendix 5.

ionic diameters when several atoms form the charged radical. Now, the Tables giving the mean activity coefficients of various electrolytes are set out in terms of molalities. To find the required molality, we write

$$I = \tfrac{1}{2}\Sigma m_i z_i^2$$

Therefore,

$$0 \cdot 1 = \tfrac{1}{2}\{m_+ z_+^2 + m_- z_-^2\}$$

Since $m_- = 2m$, and $m_+ = m$, where m is the molality of the electrolyte as a whole, we have

$$0 \cdot 1 = \tfrac{1}{2}\{(m \times 2^2) + (m \times 1^2)\} = \tfrac{1}{2}(6m) = 3m$$

Therefore $m = 0 \cdot 1/3 = 0 \cdot 0333.$*

For most uni-bivalent electrolytes, e.g. the chlorides, interpolation of available data yield ($f_\pm$) $\cong 0 \cdot 60$ to $0 \cdot 61$† while for several nitrates, the mean value is about $0 \cdot 58$, the alkali sulphates having lower values.

In view of the above considerations, the mean activity coefficient values of the chlorides should be closest to that of the $(2H^+, S^=)$ species and therefore the approximate value of $(f_\pm) \cong 0 \cdot 6$ can reasonably be adopted in this case.

Substituting the respective adopted values into the last K_3 equation, we have the approximate relation

$$\frac{0 \cdot 1}{[S^=](0 \cdot 1)^2(0 \cdot 6)^3} \cong 9 \times 10^{21}$$

and therefore $[S^=] \approx 5 \times 10^{-21}$

The result, is of course, approximate, and it is pertinent to enquire what are the advantages in upholding the use of activities instead of the simpler method of employing concentrations only. Had the latter course been adopted and the equilibrium been formulated as

$$\frac{[H_2S]}{[S^=][H^+]^2} = 9 \cdot 1 \times 10^{21}$$

and therefore $[S^=] = 1 \cdot 1 \times 10^{-21}$
i.e. the calculated result would have been about five times smaller than that calculated in terms of activities.

---

* In dilute solutions such as $0 \cdot 1$M, there is hardly any difference between molarity and molality values.

† $CdCl_2$ has a much lower value, but this is rather the exception and may well be due to complex ion formation taking place on a large scale. See also p. 29.

A further pertinent question is: What would have been the calculated result had we adopted the substitution of $(f_{\pm})_{HCl}$—for a 0·1M solution—namely the value of 0·796 for the required mean activity coefficient value? Here we have

$$\frac{0·1}{[S^=](0·1)^2(0·796)^3} \approx 9 \times 10^{21}$$

and therefore

$$[S^=] \cong 2·2 \times 10^{-21}$$

Of the two possible computations of the mean activity coefficient involved in the (2H⁺, S⁼) equilibrium, the first computation would seem to be more rigorous and therefore the more probable answer. The difficulties experienced in the assessment of the accurate value of activity coefficients illustrates the degree of uncertainty sometimes encountered.

It is possible to argue that since there often exist considerable uncertainties concerning the accuracy of the available equilibrium constant values and since such uncertainties may invalidate the degree of accuracy aimed at in the assessment to an extent greater than that involved in the application of activity coefficients, there is no advantage to be gained in inclusion of these in the calculations. It is therefore necessary to remember that there are many cases where such uncertainties do not exist. Further, since the concept of activities has been shown to be applicable in many cases, it can be be used in reverse, namely to check the correctness of uncertain values in suitable cases. Finally, if one slides into the habit of omitting activity coefficients, on the whole the calculated results are likely to be less accurate.

Example 3

The solubility product of the stable form of $Mg(OH)_2$ at 25°C and $I \gtrsim 0$ is $1·12 \times 10^{-11}$. Assess (*a*) the pH of a saturated solution of $Mg(OH)_2$ at this temperature, and (*b*) the pH at which a 0·05M $MgCl_2$, solution would begin to precipitate $Mg(OH)_2$. Assume no complex formation between the magnesium and chloride ions.

ASSESSMENT

(*a*) $Mg(OH)_2 \rightarrow Mg^{++} + 2OH^{-*}$

Let

$$[Mg^{++}] = x, \text{ then } [OH^-] = 2x$$

---

* Though these ions have been written as anhydrous ones they represent hydrated ions. The quantity of water removed from the bulk of the water available for solution is, however, truly negligible in such concentrations.

Now, the activity solubility product of $Mg(OH)_2$, at $I \gtreqless 0$ is

$$(a_{Mg^{++}})(a_{OH^-})^2 = 1\cdot1 \times 10^{-11}$$

This solubility product value is very small and suggests very low saturation concentrations where activities $\cong$ concentrations. Consequently, the concentration solubility product may be safely substituted for the activity solubility product and hence

$$[Mg^{++}][OH^-]^2 = 1\cdot1 \times 10^{-11}$$

Therefore,

$$x \times (2x)^2 = 4x^3 = 1\cdot1 \times 10^{-11}$$

Therefore,

$$x = 1\cdot4 \times 10^{-4}$$

Hence,

$$[OH^-] = 2 \times 1\cdot4 \times 10^{-4} = 2\cdot8 \times 10^{-4}$$

Now, by definition, $pH = -\log a_{H^+}$, and $K_W = (a_{H^+})(a_{OH^-}) = 1\cdot008 \times 10^{-14}$ at 25°C. However, in such very dilute solutions, the above expressions reduce to

$$pH = -\log [H^+], \text{ and } K_W = [H^+][OH^-]$$

Now,

$$[H^+] = K_W/[OH^-] = \frac{10^{-14}}{2\cdot8 \times 10^{-4}} = \frac{10^{-10}}{2\cdot8}$$

Hence, $pH \cong 10\cdot5$

The pH of a saturated solution of $Mg(OH)_2$ at 25°C has therefore a value $\sim 10\cdot5$.

(*b*) The precipitation of the $Mg(OH)_2$ will begin in presence of 0·05M $MgCl_2$ solution and therefore it is necessary to assess the value of the mean activity coefficient of $Mg(OH)_2$ in presence of such a concentration of $MgCl_2$. Examining the tables of activity coefficients we notice that at 0·05M the mean activity coefficients of $BaCl_2$ and $Ba(OH)_2$ are comparatively close, 0·56 and 0·526 respectively, and that other uni-bivalent electrolytes such as $Ca(NO_3)_2$ and $CaCl_2$ have mean activity coefficient values grouped around 0·54. We may therefore reasonably assume the mean activity coefficient of $Mg(OH)_2$ in a 0·05M $MgCl_2$ solution to be about 0·54. Hence,

$$(a_{Mg^{++}})(a_{OH^-})^2 = [Mg^{++}]f_\pm(a_{OH^-})^2$$
$$\cong 0\cdot05 \times 0\cdot54(a_{OH^-})^2 = 1\cdot1 \times 10^{-11}$$

Hence,

$$(a_{OH^-}) \cong \sqrt{\frac{1\cdot1 \times 10^{-11}}{0\cdot05 \times 0\cdot54}} \cong 2 \times 10^{-5}$$

Hence,

$$pH = - \log (a_{H^+}) = - \log(K_W/a_{OH^-}) \cong - \log \frac{10^{-14}}{2 \times 10^{-5}}$$

Therefore $pH \cong 9 \cdot 3$

i.e. the pH at which a $0 \cdot 05M$ $MgCl_2$ solution may be expected to give rise to a precipitate of magnesium hydroxide at $25°C$ is about pH $9 \cdot 3$.

Problems

1. Assuming the solubility products of AgBr at $I \gtreqless 0$ to be[81] at

5°C	$4 \cdot 11 \times 10^{-14}$
15°C	$1 \cdot 51 \times 10^{-13}$
25°C	$4 \cdot 48 \times 10^{-13}$
35°C	$1 \cdot 49 \times 10^{-12}$
45°C	$4 \cdot 06 \times 10^{-12}$

calculate (a) the solubilities at the corresponding temperatures, and (b) the heats of solution at $15°C$, $25°C$ and $35°C$.

2. Calculate (a) the solubility of silver chloride in a solution which is $0 \cdot 01M$ with respect to ammonia at equilibrium; (b) calculate the minimum concentration of ammonia which would be required to allow a total silver chloride concentration of $0 \cdot 01M$. Assume that the solubility product of AgCl at $I \gtreqless 0$, at $25°C$ is $1 \cdot 78 \times 10^{-10}$, and that the stability constant of $[Ag^+ \cdot 2NH_3]$ at $25°C$ and $I \gtreqless 0$ is $1 \cdot 3 \times 10^7$.

3. Assuming that the solubility product of $BaSO_4$ at $25°C$ and $I \gtreqless 0$ is 1×10^{-10}, calculate the solubility of $BaSO_4$ in (a) water and (b) $0 \cdot 0001N$ $BaCl_2$ solution.

4. A $0 \cdot 05M$ solution of NaCl containing $0 \cdot 001M$ K_2CrO_4 is being titrated with $0 \cdot 05N$ $AgNO_3$. Assuming the respective solubility products of AgCl and Ag_2CrO_4 to be $1 \cdot 78 \times 10^{-10}$ and $1 \cdot 3 \times 10^{-12}$ at $I \gtreqless 0$ at this temperature, assess (a) whether silver chloride or silver chromate is first precipitated and (b) the ratios $(a_{Cl^-})^2/(a_{CrO_4^=})$ and $[Cl^-]^2/[CrO_4^=]$ required for the silver chromate to begin precipitation.

5. A $0 \cdot 1M$ $BaCl_2$ solution is added to a solution which is $0 \cdot 005N$ with respect to Na_2CO_3 and $0 \cdot 005N$ with respect to Na_2SO_4. Which barium salt will be first precipitated? What will be the value of the ratio $[CO_3^=]/[SO_4^=]$ for the carbonate to begin precipitation? Assume that the solubility product values of the two electrolytes, at $I = 0$ and at $25°C$, are 1×10^{-10} for the $BaSO_4$ and $8 \cdot 1 \times 10^{-9}$ for the $BaCO_3$.

6. Calculate the ionic strengths of the following solutions

    (a) $0.1M$ HCl $+$ $0.05M$ $BaCl_2$

    (b) $0.2M$ H_2SO_4 $+$ $0.2M$ HNO_3

    (c) $0.1N$ acetic acid and $0.1N$ sodium acetate.

7. Solid AgBr and solid Ag_2CrO_4 are shaken simultaneously with a solution of Na_2CrO_4 until equilibrium is obtained when the chromate ion concentration in solution is $5 \times 10^{-3}M$. Calculate the final bromide ion concentration. Assume that the solubility products of AgBr and Ag_2CrO_4, at $I \rightleftharpoons 0$ and $25°C$ are, respectively, 4.98×10^{-13} and 1.3×10^{-12}.

8. The heats of solution of two sparingly soluble electrolytes were calculated from free energy considerations to be $+ 10$ kcal and $+ 15$ kcal respectively over the temperature range of $20°C$ to $30°C$. Calculate the respective values of the ratio

$$\frac{\text{solubility product at } 30°C}{\text{solubility product at } 20°C}$$

for the two substances.

9. The solubility product of AgOH at $25°C$ and $I \rightleftharpoons 0$ may be assumed as 2×10^{-8}. Calculate the pH of the saturated solution, and the pH at which a $0.01N$ $AgNO_3$ solution (in absence of complexing agents) begins to precipitate AgOH.

10. The activity solubility product of mercurous chloride is about 3.5×10^{-18} at a given temperature. If all the mercurous ions present are assumed to be in the form of Hg_2^{++}, assess the concentration of the chloride ion in a saturated solution of mercurous chloride at this temperature.

11. Analysis of equilibrated saturated magnesium stearate solutions $[Mg(C_{17}H_{35}CO_2)_2]$ at a certain temperature shows that 3.20 mg of Mg are present per litre of water, and 3.84 mg Mg per litre of 0.1 per cent aqueous NaCl solution. Calculate the respective concentration solubility products.

12. The solubility product values of $SrSO_4$ and $BaSO_4$, at $25°C$ and $I \rightleftharpoons 0$, are 3.2×10^{-7} and 1×10^{-10} respectively. Calculate the ratio $(a_{Ba^{++}})/(a_{Sr^{++}})$ for precipitation of $SrSO_4$ to take place. Would the precipitation ratio, if expressed in terms of concentrations instead of activities, be practically independent of the presence of other electrolytes at ionic strengths below $I = 0.01$?

13. Calculate the respective molarities required to make up solutions of $I = 0.01$, when Na_2SO_4, $BaCl_2$, $ZnSO_4$, NH_4Cl and $(NH_4)_2SO_4$ are available.

14. On substitution into the Debye-Hückel equation, the values of the geometric mean activity coefficients for uni-univalent, uni-bivalent and uni-tervalent electrolytes in aqueous solutions at 25°C are given by

$$- \log f_{\pm} = 0{\cdot}5095 \ \sqrt{\mu}$$

$$- \log f_{\pm} = 1{\cdot}0 \ \sqrt{\mu}$$

and $\quad\quad\quad - \log f_{\pm} = 1{\cdot}5 \ \sqrt{\mu}$

Calculate the mean activity coefficients of NaCl, BaCl$_2$ and La(NO$_3$)$_3$ when 1×10^{-3}M solutions of each are used.

Bibliography

CONSIDERABLE investigation has taken place, in the field of evaluation and interpretation of solubility and solubility product values, in many laboratories all over the world. The number of published papers and reviews runs into thousands, and classification and assessment of these are outside the scope of this book. Many references and quotations of solubility data and their variations, and some solubility product values may be found in Seidell's *Solubilities of Inorganic and Organic Compounds*, D. Van Nostrand Co. Inc., New York, 1940. Many data can also be found in the *International Critical Tables*, McGraw-Hill, New-York, 1928. The most comprehensive and up-to-date publication giving equilibrium constants and solubility product values is *Stability Constants*, Part II, 1958, published by the Chemical Society, London.

The references given in the next paragraphs are concerned with certain specialized topics. These are not intended to be representative nor can they be considered to do full justice to the various published investigations. The following lists should be considered merely a starting point.

Theory of the Solubility Product Principle

There have been many alternative derivations, assessments and reviews of the solubility product principle, subsequent to Nernst's original derivation, e.g.

WASHBURN, E. W., *J. Amer. chem. Soc.*, 1910, **32**, 488.
BUTLER, J. A. V., *Chem. & Ind. (Rev.)*, 1924, **28**, 634.
BUTLER, J. A. V., *J. phys. Chem.*, 1924, **28**, 438.
PARTINGTON, J. R., in *A Treatise on Physical Chemistry* Vol. I, ed. H. S. Taylor, Macmillan and Co., Lond., 1931, p. 702.
DENBIGH, K. G., *J. chem. Ed.*, 1941, **18**, 126.

Other assessments may be found in several textbooks on analytical chemistry.

None of these consider the solubility product principle in terms of the *comprehensive* solubility product equation. The first papers to consider this are by

LEWIN, S., *Lab. Prac.*, 1957, **6**, 573.
LEWIN, S., ibid., 1957, **6**, 642.
LEWIN, S., ibid., 1958, **7**, 637.

Ageing and Phase Nucleation

Many aspects of the well-known alterations in appearance and behaviour of precipitates on standing or ageing and on aspects of phase nucleation have been considered by—

OSTWALD, W. Z., *The Scientific Foundations of Analytical Chemistry*, (transl. by M'Gowan), Macmillan, Lond., 1908.
SMITS, A., *Theory of Allotropy*, Longmans, Lond., 1922.
TAMMANN, G., *The States of Aggregation*, Constable, Lond., 1926.
MAY, D. R. and KOLTHOFF, I. M., *J. phys. Chem.*, 1948, **52**, 836.
KOLTHOFF, I. M., International Congress of Analytical Chemistry, 1952.
Discussions of the Faraday Society, *Crystal Growth*, 1949.
BRADLEY, R. S., *Quart. Rev. chem. Soc., Lond.*, 1951, V, p. 315.

Precipitations in Qualitative Analysis

Most of the advanced textbooks on qualitative analysis devote some space to interpreting the precipitations in terms of the concentration solubility product principle on the tacit assumption that equilibrium conditions exist. Assessment of the precipitation of certain Groups is given by

BRITTON, H. T. S., *Hydrogen Ions*, Chapman & Hall, Lond., 1942.
HAMMETT, L. P., *Solutions of Electrolytes*, McGraw-Hill, 1936.

The precipitation of sulphides in Group II has received considerable attention owing to the various difficulties encountered. Critical reviews of published solubilities of metal sulphides in water are given by

KOLTHOFF, I. M., *J. phys. Chem.*, 1931, **35**, 2711.
RAVITZ, S. F., *J. phys. Chem.*, 1936, **40**, 61.
RINGBOM, A., *Solubilities of Sulphides*, Report to Analytical Section I I.U.P.A.C., July, 1953.

Basic Salts

W. Feitknecht's papers on basic salts and the interaction of substances in liquids should be consulted. They were published in

Helv. chim. Acta, 1926, **9**, 1018.
ibid., 1927, **10**, 140.
ibid., 1930, **13**, 1380.
ibid., 1933, **16**, 1302.

In these papers and others X-ray evidence and other considerations were utilized by Feitknecht in his investigations of the ageing of basic zinc, and other, salts.

Calculations on, and assessment of the significance of, the solubility products of hydroxides of metals which form basic salts have been carried out by

HUME, D. N., and STONE, H. W., *J. Amer. chem. Soc.*, 1941, **63**, 1197.

GELOSO, M., and DESCHAMPS, P., *C.R. Acad. Sci., Paris*, 1947, **224**, 1163.

For a review of basic salts consult

BASSETT, H., *Quart. Rev. chem. Soc., Lond.*, 1947, **I**, p. 246.

Hydration of Ions

Ion solvation is discussed in electrochemistry books. The following, however, deal extensively in ion hydration

BELL, R. P., Hydration of Ions in Solution, *Endeavour*, Jan. 1958, p. 31.

GURNEY, R. W., *Ionic Processes in Solution*, McGraw-Hill, 1953.

Discussions of the Faraday Society *Interaction in Ionic Solutions*, 1957.

BOCKRIS, J. O'M., *Quart. Rev. chem. Soc., Lond.*, 1949, **3**, 179.

Complex Salt Formation

Information concerning this aspect is found scattered in many textbooks of analytical chemistry. N. BJERRUM's book *Metal-ammine Formation in Aqueous Solution. Theory of Reversible Step Reactions*, Haase and Son, Copenhagen, 1941, is an important contribution in this field.

Determination of Solubility Product Values

Considerable information concerning such determinations can be found in advanced analytical chemistry textbooks and books on electrochemistry. The following will be found useful in the above connexion or in connexion with the evaluation of activity coefficient values.

FUOSS, R. M., *J. Amer. chem. Soc.*, 1957, **79**, 3301.

LATIMER, W. M., *Oxidation Potentials*, 2nd ed., Prentice-Hall, New York, 1952.

HARNED, H. S., and OWEN, B. B., *The Physical Chemistry of Electrolytic Solutions*, 2nd ed., Reinhold Publishing Corp., 1950.

LEWIS, G. N., and RANDALL, M., *Thermodynamics and the Free Energy of Chemical Substances*, McGraw-Hill, New York, 1923.

References

1. NERNST, *Z. phys. Chem.*, 1889, **4**, 372.
2. e.g. BATHRICK, *J. phys. Chem.*, 1896–7, **1**, 157; TAYLOR, ibid., 1896–7, **1**, 720.
3. HILDEBRAND, *Solubility*, p. 165, Reinhold Publishing Corp., 1936.
4. NOYES, *Z. phys. Chem.*, 1890, **6**, 241.
5. NOYES, *Z. phys. Chem.*, 1895, **16**, 125; ibid., 1898, **26**, 152.
6. KENDALL, *Proc. roy. Soc.*, 1911, **85A**, 200.
7. HARKINS and PEARCE, *J. Amer. chem. Soc.*, 1916, **38**, 2679.
8. STIEGLITZ, *J. Amer. chem. Soc.*, 1908, **30**, 946.
9. BRØNSTED and LAMER, *J. Amer. chem. Soc.*, 1924, **46**, 555.
10. DEBYE and HÜCKEL, *Z. Physik.*, 1923, **24**, 185, 305; ibid., 1924, **25**, 145.
11. BRØNSTED, *J. Amer. chem. Soc.*, 1922, **44**, 877; ibid., 1923, **45**, 2898.
12. LEWIN, *Lab. Pract.*, 1957, **6**, 573.
13. POPOFF and NEUMANN, *J. phys. Chem.*, 1930, **34**, 1853.
14. NEUMANN, *J. Amer. chem. Soc.*, 1933, **55**, 879.
15. HAMMARSTEN, *C.R. Lab. Carlsberg*, 1929, **17**, No. 11.
16. LEWIS, G. N. and RANDALL, M., *Thermodynamics and the Free Energy of Chemical Substances*, p. 282, McGraw-Hill, New York, 1923.
17. LEWIN, *Lab. Pract.*, 1957, **6**, 642.
18. KOLTHOFF and EGGERSTON, *J. Amer. chem. Soc.*, 1939, **61**, 1036.
19. BASSETT, H., *Quart. Rev. chem. Soc., Lond.*, 1947, **1**, 246.
20. LEWIN, *Lab. Pract.*, 1958, **7**, 637.
21. BRITTON and DODD, *J. chem. Soc.*, 1932, 1940.
22. For references see BRITTON, *Hydrogen Ions*, Vol. II, 3rd ed., p. 159, Chapman and Hall, 1942.
23. SCHANOV, *Z. phys. Chem.*, 1913, **83**, 129.
24. BJERRUM, *Kgl. Danske Vidersk. Skelskab.*, 1926, **7**, No. 9.
25. FUOSS, R. M., *Chem. Rev.*, 1935, **17**, 27.
26. FUOSS, R. M., *J. Amer. chem. Soc.*, 1934, **56**, 2017.
27. FUOSS, R. M., and KRAUS, ibid., 1935, **57**, 1.
28. FUOSS, R. M., and KRAUS, ibid., 1933, **55**, 2387.
29. FUOSS, R. M., and KRAUS, ibid., 1933, **55**, 1019.
30. BELCHER, *J. and Proc. Roy. Inst. Chem.*, 1949, Part II, p. 101.
31. RILEY and GALLOFONT, *J. chem. Soc.*, 1932, 514.
32. RIGHELLATO and DAVIES, *Trans. Faraday Soc.*, 1930, **26**, 592.
33. BATES and VOSBURGH, *J. Amer. chem. Soc.*, 1937, **59**, 1583.

34. GLASSTONE, S., *J. chem. Soc.*, 1921, **119**, 1689, 1914.
35. BRITTON and ROBINSON, *Trans. Faraday Soc.*, 1932, **28**, 531.
36. BRITTON, *Hydrogen Ions*, Vol. II, p. 47, Chapman and Hall, Lond., 1942.
37. BÖTTGER, Z. *phys. Chem.*, 1903, **46**, 521; ibid., 1906, **56**, 83.
38. WHITBY, Z. *anorg. Chem.*, 1910, **67**, 107.
39. BJERRUM, *Laerbog i. Uorganisk Kemi*, 4th ed., p. 297, 1937; Ph.D. Thesis, *Studien over basiske Kromiforbindelser*, Copenhagen, 1908.
40. LAMB and JACQUES, *J. Amer. chem. Soc.*, 1938, **60**, 1215.
41. BRØNSTED and VOLQUARTZ, Z. *phys. Chem.*, 1928, **134**, 97.
42. BJERRUM, *Naturwissenschaften*, 1926, **5**, 129.
43. LAMB and DAMON, *J. Amer. chem. Soc.*, 1937, **59**, 383.
44. GJALDBAECK, Z. *anorg. Chem.*, 1934, **218**, 113.
45. KILDE, Z. *anorg. Chem.*, 1934, **218**, 113.
46. DAVIES, *J. chem. Soc.*, 1935, 910.
47. O'SULLIVAN, *Trans. Faraday Soc.*, 1925–6, **21**, 319.
48. QUINTIN, *J. Chim. phys.*, 1927, **24**, 715.
49. MCDOWELL and JOHNSTON, *J. Amer. chem. Soc.*, 1936, **58**, 2009.
50. JOHNSTON, CUTA and GARRETT, *J. Amer. chem. Soc.*, 1933, **55**, 2311.
51. LAUE, Z. *anorg. Chem.*, 1927, **165**, 325; GARRETT and HIRSCHLER, *J. Amer. chem. Soc.*, 1938, **60**, 299.
52. PRYTZ, Z. *anorg. Chem.*, 1931, **200**, 133.
53. LEY, Z. *phys. Chem.*, 1899, **30**, 249.
54. RAVITZ, *J. phys. Chem.*, 1936, **40**, 61.
55. BRUNER and ZAWADSKY, Z. *anorg. Chem.*, 1910, **65**, 136.
56. BRUNER and ZAWADSKY, Z. *anorg. Chem.*, 1910, **67**, 454.
57. HARNED and HAMER, *J. Amer. chem. Soc.*, 1933, **55**, 2194; HARNED and MANNWEILER, ibid., 1935, **57**, 1875; HARNED and GEARY, ibid., 1937, **59**, 2032; HARNED and DONELSON, ibid., 1937, **59**, 1280; HARNED and OWEN, *The Physical Chemistry of Electrolytic Solutions*, 2nd ed., Reinhold Publishing Corp., New York, 1950.
58. BANCROFT, *J. Phys. u. Chemie*, 1896, **1**, 142.
59. OSTWALD, Z. *phys. Chem.*, 1897, **22**, 306.
60. TAMMANN, ibid., 1898, **25**, 422.
61. VON WEIMARN, *Zur Lehre von den Zustanden der Materie*, p. 83, 1914; *Chem. Rev.*, 1926, **2**, 217.
62. DUNDON, *J. Amer. chem. Soc.*, 1923, **45**, 2658.
63. HULLET, Z. *phys. Chem.*, 1901, **37**, 385; ibid., 1904, **47**, 357.
64. HULLET and DUSCHAK, Z. *anorg. Chem.*, 1904, **40**, 196.
65. JOHNSON and ADAMS, *J. Amer. chem. Soc.*, 1911, **33**, 829.
66. OSTWALD, Z. *phys. Chem.*, 1900, **34**, 503.
67. FREUNDLICH, *Colloid and Capillary Chemistry*, p. 155, Methuen & Co., Lond., 1926.
68. A similar equation has been developed by JONES, Z. *phys. Chem.*, 1913, **82**, 448.
69. DUNDON and MACK, *J. Amer. chem. Soc.*, 1923, **45**, 2479.
70. KNAPP, *Trans. Faraday Soc.*, 1921, **17**, 457.

71. MAY and KOLTHOFF, *J. phys. Chem.*, 1948, **52**, 836.
72. DAWSON, *Annual Reports on the Progress of Chemistry*, 1924, **21**, 24.
73. LANGE and MESSNER, *Naturwissenschaften.*, 1922, **15**, 54.
74. LANGE and ROBINSON, *Chem. Rev.*, 1931, **9**, 89.
75. ROBINSON and WALLACE, *J. Amer. chem. Soc.*, 1932, **54**, 1311, 1320, *Chem. Rev.*, 1942, **30**, 195.
76. *International Critical Tables*, Vol. III, p. 370, McGraw-Hill, New York, 1928. ·
77. PARTINGTON, J. R., *Text-book of Inorganic Chemistry*, 5th ed., p. 319, Macmillan, Lond., 1946; PARTINGTON, J. R., *A Treatise on Physical Chemistry*, ed. H. S. Taylor, p. 702, Macmillan, New York, 1931.
78. MILONE and FERRERO, *Gazz. chim. ital.*, 1947, **77**, 3485.
79. BUNN, *Proc. Roy. Soc.*, 1933, **A141**, 567.
80. OWEN, J. *Amer. chem. Soc.*, 1938, **60**, 2229.
81. OWEN and BRINKLEY, ibid., 1938, **60**, 2233.
82. LEWIN, *J. chem. Educ.*, 1953, **30**, 136.
83. FORBES and COLE, *J. Amer. chem. Soc.*, 1921, **43**, 2492.
84. BARNEY, ARGERSINGER and REYNOLDS, *J. Amer. chem. Soc.*, 1951, **73**, 3785, according to *Stability Constants*, Part II, p. 101, the Chemical Society, Lond., 1958.
85. THIEL and GESSNER, *Z. anorg. Chem.*, 1914, **86**, 1.
86. GOATES, GORDON and FAUX, *J. Amer. chem. Soc.*, 1952, **74**, 835.
87. SÖRENSEN, *C.R. Lab. Carlsberg*, 1909, **8**, 1.
88. SÖRENSEN, *Z. Biochem.*, 1909, **21**, 131, 201.
89. CLARK, *The Determination of Hydrogen Ions*, 3rd ed., p. 461, Williams and Wilkins, Baltimore, 1928.
90. KOLTHOFF, *Rec. Trav. chim. Pays-Bas*, 1930, **49**, 401.
91. ENGEL, *C.R. Acad. Sci.*, Paris, 1887, **104**, 507, 913.
92. AKERLOF and SHORT, *J. Amer. chem. Soc.*, 1937, **59**, 1912.
93. MILLIGAN, *J. phys. Chem.*, 1934, **38**, 797.
94. MELLOR, *Modern Inorganic Chemistry*, p. 233, Longmans, 1940.
95. INGHAM, *J. chem. Soc.*, 1928, **131**, 1917.
96. GLASSTONE, S., *Textbook of Physical Chemistry*, 2nd ed., Macmillan, Lond., 1948.
97. GLASSTONE, S., *Thermodynamics for Chemists*, p. 420, D. Van Nostrand Co. Inc., New York, 1947.
98. CHATTAWAY, *J. Amer. chem. Soc.*, 1916, **38**, 2519.

Solutions to Problems

1. Assuming complete ionization, we have in the saturated solution

$$AgBr \rightarrow Ag^+ + Br^-$$

Hence the solubility of AgBr equals that of the bromide ion or the silver ion, i.e.,

$$[AgBr] = [Ag^+] = [Br^-]$$

Now $\quad (a_{Ag^+})(a_{Br^-}) = K$

$$= [Ag^+]f_{Ag^+}[Br^-]f_{Br^-}$$

$$= [Ag^+][Br^-](f_{\pm})^2$$

But at $\quad I \gtrless 0$, $(f_{\pm}) = 1$,

Therefore, $[Ag^+][Br^-] = K$

$\therefore \quad [AgBr] = [Ag^+] = \sqrt{K}.$

It follows that at

$$25°C \quad [AgBr] = \sqrt{4 \cdot 11 \times 10^{-14}} = 2 \cdot 03 \times 10^{-7} \text{ moles per litre}$$

$$15°C \quad [AgBr] = \sqrt{1 \cdot 51 \times 10^{-13}} = 3 \cdot 87 \times 10^{-7} \text{ moles per litre}$$

$$25°C \quad [AgBr] = \sqrt{4 \cdot 48 \times 10^{-13}} = 6 \cdot 69 \times 10^{-7} \text{ moles per litre}$$

$$35°C \quad [AgBr] = \sqrt{1 \cdot 49 \times 10^{-12}} = 1 \cdot 22 \times 10^{-6} \text{ moles per litre}$$

$$45°C \quad [AgBr] = \sqrt{4 \cdot 06 \times 10^{-12}} = 2 \cdot 02 \times 10^{-6} \text{ moles per litre}$$

The heat of solution may be calculated by plotting $\log K$ against $1/T$ and evaluating the slope, when $\Delta H = 2 \cdot 303 \times R \times$ slope. When the slope is not exactly a straight line but somewhat curved, the tangent to the curve at the particular temperature gives the exact value of ΔH. Alternatively, the relation

$$\Delta H = \frac{2 \cdot 303 R T_1 T_2}{T_2 - T_1} \log (K_2/K_1)$$

may be employed.

For accuracy T_2 should be above T as much as T_1 is below it, and dT

should be as small as possible. The data given allow however only a five degrees difference and hence ΔH calculated is only approximate.

$$\Delta H_{15°C} = 2\cdot303 \times 1\cdot986 \frac{(278\cdot1 \times 298\cdot1)}{(25 - 5)} \times \log\left\{\frac{4\cdot48 \times 10^{-13}}{4\cdot1 \times 10^{-14}}\right\}$$

$$= 19\cdot7 \text{ kcal}$$

$$\Delta H_{25°C} = 2\cdot303 \times 1\cdot986 \frac{(288\cdot1 \times 308\cdot1)}{(35 - 15)} \log\left\{\frac{1\cdot49 \times 10^{-12}}{1\cdot51 \times 10^{-13}}\right\}$$

$$= 21\cdot6 \text{ kcal}$$

$$\Delta H_{35°C} = 2\cdot303 \times 1\cdot986 \frac{(298\cdot1 \times 318\cdot1)}{(45 - 25)} \log\left\{\frac{4\cdot06 \times 10^{-12}}{4\cdot48 \times 10^{-13}}\right\}$$

$$= 23\cdot5 \text{ kcal}$$

2(a).
$$(a_{Ag^+})(a_{Cl^-}) = 1\cdot78 \times 10^{-10} \quad . \qquad . \qquad . \qquad \text{(i)}$$

$$\frac{(a_{(Ag^+\cdot2NH_3)})}{(a_{Ag^+})(a_{NH_3})^2} = 1\cdot3 \times 10^7 \quad . \qquad . \qquad . \qquad \text{(ii)}$$

The solubility of silver chloride equals the expression

$$[Ag^+] + [Ag^+\cdot2NH_3]$$

Owing to the magnitude of the stability constant, $[Ag^+\cdot2NH_3] \ggg [Ag^+]$, and therefore the solubility of the silver chloride may be taken as being practically equal to that of the silver diammine ion, i.e.

$$[Ag^+\cdot2NH_3] = [\text{Silver chloride}] \quad . \qquad . \qquad \text{(iii)}$$

It follows that

$$[Ag^+\cdot2NH_3] = [Cl^-] \quad . \qquad . \qquad . \qquad \text{(iiia)}$$

Therefore, rewriting equation (i), we have

$$[Ag^+][Ag^+\cdot2NH_3](f_{\pm})^2 = 1\cdot78 \times 10^{-10} \quad . \qquad . \qquad \text{(iv)}$$

Ionic strength contributions: The ammonia present gives rise to NH_4^+ and OH^- ions; in $0\cdot01M$ ammonia solution their concentrations are in the region of 10^{-4} molar. The ionic concentrations due to the dissolved silver, silver diammine and chloride ions are also in the region of $10^{-4}M$. Allowing for the total ionic concentrations approaching a concentration of $10^{-3}M$, the value of $(f_{\pm})$ will be in the region of $0\cdot97$ or over. Therefore, allowing for the involved percentage error in neglecting the activity coefficient, we may approximate equation (iv) to

$$[Ag^+][Ag^+\cdot2NH_3] \cong 1\cdot78 \times 10^{-10} \quad . \qquad . \qquad . \qquad \text{(v)}$$

In the case of equation (ii), substituting for activities and allowing for the general case that the activity coefficients of non-electrolytes are, in such dilute solution, practically equal to unity, we have

$$\frac{[Ag^+\cdot2NH_3] \times f_{Ag^+\cdot2NH_3}}{[Ag^+] \times f_{Ag^+}[NH_3]^2} = 1\cdot3 \times 10^7 \quad . \qquad . \qquad \text{(iia)}$$

Now, the two activity coefficients, even if they are not equal to unity, should—by the Lewis-Randall generalization—in such dilute solutions be equal to one another, hence

$$\frac{[Ag^+ \cdot 2NH_3]}{[Ag^+](0 \cdot 01)^2} = 1 \cdot 3 \times 10^7 \qquad . \qquad . \qquad . \text{ (iib)}$$

Multiplying (iib) by (v), we have

$$[Ag^+ \cdot 2NH_3]^2 = (1 \cdot 78 \times 10^{-10})(1 \cdot 3 \times 10^3)$$

Therefore $\qquad [Ag^+ \cdot 2NH_3] \cong 4 \cdot 8 \times 10^{-4}$ moles per litre,

i.e. the concentration of the silver chloride dissolved at equilibrium with a 0·01M ammonia solution is approximately $4 \cdot 8 \times 10^{-4}$ moles per litre. The result is approximate to the extent of the various assumptions involved.

Alternatively, the above calculation may be formulated as follows— Electrical neutrality requires that

$$[Cl^-] = [Ag^+] + [Ag^+ \cdot 2NH_3]$$

Therefore, by equation (i),

$$[Ag^+]\{[Ag^+] + [Ag^+ \cdot 2NH_3]\} = 1 \cdot 78 \times 10^{-10}$$

Hence, $\qquad [Ag^+]^2\{1 + 1 \cdot 3 \times 10^7[NH_3]^2\} = 1 \cdot 78 \times 10^{-10}$

assuming $\qquad f_{Ag^+ \cdot 2NH_3} = f_{Ag^+}.$

whence $\qquad [Ag^+]^2 = \dfrac{1 \cdot 78 \times 10^{-10}}{1 + (1 \cdot 3 \times 10^7 \times 10^{-4})} = \dfrac{1 \cdot 78}{1 \cdot 3} \times 10^{-13}$

(correct to the second decimal)

$$\therefore \qquad [Ag^+] = \sqrt{\frac{17 \cdot 8}{1 \cdot 3}} \times 10^{-7}$$

$$\therefore \qquad [Cl^-] = \frac{1 \cdot 78 \times 10^{-10}}{\sqrt{\dfrac{17 \cdot 8}{1 \cdot 3}} \times 10^{-7}} \cong 4 \cdot 81 \times 10^{-4}$$

And this, last, value equals the solubility of silver chloride in the given ammonia solution.

2(*b*). Putting [Silver chloride] = $[Cl^-] = 10^{-2}$, we have

$$(Ag^+)(f_\pm)^2 = \frac{1 \cdot 78 \times 10^{-10}}{10^{-2}} = 1 \cdot 78 \times 10^{-8}$$

The solubility of silver chloride is given as 10^{-2}. The activity coefficient value of uni-univalent ions, when $I = 0 \cdot 01$, is 0·899 by the Debye-Hückel equation, at 25°C. However, the corresponding values of the activity coefficients of most uni-univalent electrolytes are over 0·9. Assuming that we use the value of $f_\pm = 0 \cdot 9$, then $[Ag^+] = \dfrac{1 \cdot 78 \times 10^{-8}}{0 \cdot 81}$

Using the same arguments which resulted in equation (iib), we have

$$\frac{[Ag^+ \cdot 2NH_3]}{[Ag^+][NH_3]^2} = 1 \cdot 3 \times 10^7$$

But $[Ag^+ \cdot 2NH_3] \cong [Cl^-] = 10^{-2}$

Therefore,

$$\frac{10^{-2}}{\left(\dfrac{1 \cdot 78 \times 10^{-8}}{0 \cdot 81}\right) \times 1 \cdot 3 \times 10^7} \cong [NH_3]^2$$

Hence, $[NH_3] \cong 0 \cdot 19M$

i.e. an approximately $0 \cdot 19M$ ammonia solution is required to be present at equilibrium for the overall solubility of silver chloride to be 10^{-2} molar.

3(*a*). $[Ba^{++}][SO_4^=] \times (f_\pm)^2 = 1 \times 10^{-10}$

Such a solubility product value is associated, in binary salts, with ionic concentrations in the region of 10^{-5} molar. Hence, we may safely write $f_\pm = 1 \cdot 0$. Now, for electrical neutrality,

$$[Ba^{++}] = [SO_4^=] = \sqrt{10^{-10}} = 10^{-5}$$

i.e. the solubility of $BaSO_4$ is 10^{-5} moles per litre.

3(*b*). $[Ba^{++}]_{total} = [Ba^{++}]_{BaCl_2} + [Ba^{++}]_{BaSO_4}$

Therefore,

$$\{[Ba^{++}]_{SO_4^=} + 10^{-4}\} \times [SO_4^=] \cong 10^{-10}$$

since in such dilute solutions $f_\pm \cong 1$.

Let $[SO_4^=] = x$, then $\{10^{-4} + x\}x \cong 10^{-10}$

Hence $10^{-4}x + x^2 \cong 10^{-10}$

Therefore $x \cong 5 \times 10^{-5}$

i.e. the solubility of $BaSO_4$ in a $10^{-4}M$ $BaCl_2$ is approximately 5×10^{-5} moles per litre.

4(*a*). $[Ag^+][Cl^-](f_\pm)^2_{AgCl} \geq 1 \cdot 78 \times 10^{-10}$.   .   (1)

for AgCl to precipitate.

$$[Ag^+]^2[CrO_4^=](f_\pm)^3_{Ag_2CrO_4} \geq 1 \cdot 3 \times 10^{-12} \qquad . \quad . \quad (2)$$

for Ag_2CrO_4 to precipitate. For uni-univalent electrolytes at $0 \cdot 05$ normality, $f_\pm$ varies between $0 \cdot 81$ to $0 \cdot 84$ approximately. Assuming we take the approximate value of $(f_\pm)_{AgCl}$ as $0 \cdot 83$ and the approximate value of $(f_\pm)_{Ag_2CrO_4}$ as $0 \cdot 53$ (based on parallel considerations), then
          Equation (1) gives

$$[Ag^+]_{AgCl} = \frac{1 \cdot 78 \times 10^{-10}}{[Cl^-](f_\pm)^2_{AgCl}} = \frac{1 \cdot 78 \times 10^{-10}}{0 \cdot 05 \times (0 \cdot 83)^2}$$

Equation (2) gives

$$[Ag^+]_{Ag_2CrO_4} = \sqrt{\frac{1\cdot3 \times 10^{-12}}{[CrO_4^=](f_\pm)^3_{Ag_2CrO_4}}} = \sqrt{\frac{1\cdot3 \times 10^{-12}}{10^{-2}(0\cdot53)^3}}$$

The solubility of silver chloride being lower than that of the chromate, silver chloride will be first precipitated.

4(*b*). For the silver chromate to begin precipitation

$$(a_{Ag^+})^2(a_{CrO_4^=}) \geq 1\cdot3 \times 10^{-12} \qquad . \qquad . \qquad . \qquad (3)$$

$$\therefore \qquad (a_{Ag^+})^2 \geq \frac{1\cdot3 \times 10^{-12}}{(a_{CrO_4^=})} \qquad . \qquad . \qquad . \qquad (3a)$$

For the AgCl to stop precipitation,

$$(a_{Ag^+})(a_{Cl^-}) \leq 1\cdot78 \times 10^{-10} \qquad . \qquad . \qquad . \qquad (4)$$

$$\therefore \qquad (a_{Ag^+})^2 \leq \frac{(1\cdot78 \times 10^{-10})^2}{(a_{Cl^-})^2} \qquad . \qquad . \qquad . \qquad (3b)$$

Now, when the silver chromate precipitation begins, the activity of the silver ions must be the same whether the chromate or chloride equilibrium is considered, hence

$$\frac{1\cdot3 \times 10^{-12}}{(a_{CrO})} \approx \frac{(1\cdot78 \times 10^{-10})^2}{(a_{Cl^-})^2}$$

Therefore,

$$\frac{(a_{Cl^-})^2}{(a_{CrO_4^=})} \approx \frac{(1\cdot78 \times 10^{-10})^2}{1\cdot3 \times 10^{-12}}, \quad \text{i.e.} \approx 2\cdot4 \times 10^{-8}$$

Now, before precipitation the solution was 0·05M with respect to NaCl. As the reaction of NaCl with AgNO$_3$ proceeded precipitation of NaCl followed, but this resulted merely in substitution of the nitrate ion for the chloride and hence the ionic strength retained its original value of 0·05. Examining the Tables of activity coefficients for values for uni-univalent electrolytes at 0·05M we note an approximate, average, value of $f_\pm = 0\cdot82$, while for bi-univalent electrolytes such as K$_2$SO$_4$, Na$_2$SO$_4$ and BaCl$_2$ the average value lies in the region of 0·5 to 0·6. Choosing a *rough* value of 0·55 for the mean activity coefficient of Ag$_2$CrO$_4$, we obtain

$$\frac{[Cl^-]^2 \times (0\cdot82)^2}{[CrO_4^=] \times 0\cdot55} \approx 2\cdot4 \times 10^{-8}$$

Hence, $\dfrac{[Cl^-]^2}{[CrO_4^=]} = 2\cdot4 \times 10^{-8} \times \dfrac{0\cdot55}{(0\cdot82)^2}$, i.e. $\approx 2 \times 10^{-8}$

5. $(a_{Ba^{++}})(a_{SO_4^=}) = [Ba^{++}][SO_4^=](f_\pm)^2_{BaSO_4} = 10^{-10}$ . . . (i)

$(a_{Ba^{++}})(a_{CO_3^=}) = [Ba^{++}][CO_3^=](f_\pm)^2_{BaCO_3} = 8\cdot1 \times 10^{-9}$. (ii)

Now, in the comparatively dilute solutions used

$$(f_\pm)_{BaSO_4} \cong (f_\pm)_{BaCO_3} \qquad . \qquad . \qquad . \qquad \text{(iii)}$$

Also

$$[SO_4^=] = [CO_3^=] = \frac{0 \cdot 005_M}{2}$$

Therefore

$$\frac{[Ba^{++}]_{SO_4^=}[SO_4^=](f_\pm)^2_{BaSO_4}}{[Ba^{++}]_{CO_3^=}[CO_3^=](f_\pm)^2_{BaCO_3}} = \frac{10^{-10}}{8 \cdot 1 \times 10^{-9}}$$

$$= \frac{[Ba^{++}]_{SO_4^=}}{[Ba^{++}]_{CO_3^=}} = \frac{10^{-10}}{8 \cdot 1 \times 10^{-9}}$$

i.e. the Ba^{++} in the form of $BaSO_4$ is smaller than that of the $BaCO_3$. Hence, $BaSO_4$ will be precipitated first.

Rewriting the first two equations we have

$$(f_\pm)^2_{BaSO_4} = \frac{10^{-10}}{[Ba^{++}][SO_4^=]} \quad \text{and} \quad (f_\pm)^2_{BaCO_3} = \frac{8 \cdot 1 \times 10^{-9}}{[Ba^{++}][CO_3^=]}$$

Utilizing equation (iii), we have

$$\frac{10^{-10}}{[Ba^{++}][SO_4^=]} = \frac{8 \cdot 1 \times 10^{-9}}{[Ba^{++}][CO_3^=]}$$

The Ba^{++}, being the total barium ion concentration in solution, has the same value in both cases, therefore

$$\frac{[CO_3^=]}{[SO_4^=]} = \frac{8 \cdot 1 \times 10^{-9}}{10^{-10}} = 81$$

i.e. the barium carbonate will begin precipitation when the sulphate ion concentration will have been reduced (after precipitation as $BaSO_4$) to such an extent that the above ratio will have been reached.

6. $\qquad I = 0 \cdot 5 \, \Sigma m_i z_i^2$

Therefore, in (a) $I = 0 \cdot 5 \, \{0 \cdot 1(1)^2 + 0 \cdot 1(1)^2 + 0 \cdot 05(2)^2 + 2 \times 0 \cdot 05(1)^2\}$

$$= 0 \cdot 5 \, \{0 \cdot 1 + 0 \cdot 1 + 0 \cdot 3\} = 0 \cdot 25$$

In (b) $\qquad I = 0 \cdot 5\{[2 \times 0 \cdot 2(1)^2] + [0 \cdot 2(2)^2] + [0 \cdot 2(1)^2] + [0 \cdot 2(1)^2]\}$

$$= 0 \cdot 8$$

In (c), the dissociation constant of acetic acid is very small (about $1 \cdot 8 \times 10^{-5}$) consequently, its dissociation is quite small and in presence of the salt it is considerably smaller. Hence, the ionic contribution of acetic acid can be safely neglected.

$$I = \tfrac{1}{2}\{0 \cdot 1(1)^2 + 0 \cdot 1(1)^2\}$$

7. At equilibrium $(a_{Ag^+})^2(a_{CrO_4^=}) = 1 \cdot 3 \times 10^{-12} \qquad . \qquad . \qquad . \qquad \text{(i)}$

and $\qquad (a_{Ag^+})(a_{Br^-}) = 4 \cdot 98 \times 10^{-13} \qquad . \qquad . \qquad . \qquad \text{(ii)}$

Also, $\qquad [CrO_4^=] = 5 \times 10^{-3}$

Rewriting (i) we obtain

$$[Ag^+]^2 \times 5 \times 10^{-3} \times (f_\pm)^3_{AgCrO_4} = 1\cdot3 \times 10^{-12} \qquad (ia)$$

Assuming that the electrolyte in solution is composed mainly of Na_2CrO_4, and assuming that the activity coefficient of Ag_2CrO_4 in such a solution is practically the same as the average of other similar uni-univalent electrolytes, viz. about 0·78, we have

$$[Ag^+]^2 = \frac{1\cdot3 \times 10^{-12}}{5 \times 10^{-3} \times (0\cdot78)^3} = \frac{1\cdot3 \times 10^{-9}}{5 \times (0\cdot78)^3}$$

Now, the activity coefficients of uni-univalent electrolytes in their 0·005M solutions is about 0·93. Hence, substituting these values in equation (ii), we have

$$[Br^-] = \frac{4\cdot98 \times 10^{-13}}{\left\{\dfrac{1\cdot3 \times 10^{-9}}{5 \times (0\cdot78)^3}\right\} \times (0\cdot93)^2}$$

$$= 1\cdot12 \times 10^{-3} \text{ (to the second decimal)}$$

This result is, of course, approximate because of the approximate values of the activity coefficients.

8. $\qquad \log (K_2/K_1) = \dfrac{\Delta H}{2\cdot303R}\left\{\dfrac{1}{T_1} - \dfrac{1}{T_2}\right\}$

Hence, $\qquad K_2/K_1 = \text{antilog}\left\{\dfrac{\Delta H}{2\cdot303R}\left(\dfrac{1}{T_1} - \dfrac{1}{T_2}\right)\right\}$

For the sparingly soluble electrolyte with $\Delta H = +15$ kcal, the equation becomes

$$K_2/K_1 = \text{antilog}\left\{\dfrac{15,000}{2\cdot303 \times 1\cdot986}\left(\dfrac{1}{293\cdot1} - \dfrac{1}{303\cdot1}\right)\right\}$$

$$= \text{antilog} (0\cdot3673)$$

$$= 2\cdot330$$

For the second sparingly soluble electrolyte with $\Delta H = 10$ kcal, we have

$$K_2/K_1 = \text{antilog}\left\{\dfrac{10,000}{2\cdot303 \times 1\cdot986}\left(\dfrac{1}{293\cdot1} - \dfrac{1}{303\cdot1}\right)\right\}$$

$$= \text{antilog} (0\cdot2437)$$

$$= 1\cdot753$$

9. $$(a_{Ag^+})(a_{OH^-}) = 2 \times 10^{-8}$$

Putting $(a_{OH^-}) = (a_{Ag^+})$, we obtain $(a_{OH^-})^2 = 2 \times 10^{-8}$

Hence, $$a_{OH^-} = \sqrt{2 \times 10^{-8}} = 1\cdot414 \times 10^{-4}$$

Now, $$(a_{OH^-})(a_{H^+}) = 1\cdot008 \times 10^{-14}$$

Hence, $$a_{H^+} = \frac{1\cdot008 \times 10^{-14}}{1\cdot414 \times 10^{-4}}$$

$$pH = -\log a_{H^+} = -(\overline{11}\cdot8427) \simeq 10\cdot16$$

The Debye-Hückel limiting equation gives, for uni-univalent electrolytes in $0\cdot01M$ solutions, $(f_\pm) = 0\cdot89$. Many uni-univalent electrolytes, however, have at this concentration $(f_\pm)$ values greater than $0\cdot9$. Choosing an intermediate value of $(f_\pm) = 0\cdot9$, we may write

$$(0\cdot01 \times 0\cdot9)(a_{OH^-}) = 2 \times 10^{-8}$$

$$a_{OH^-} = \frac{2 \times 10^{-8}}{0\cdot01 \times 0\cdot9} = \frac{2}{9} \times 10^{-5}$$

$$pH = -\log a_{H^+} = -\log(K_w/[OH^-])$$

$$= -\log\left\{\frac{1 \times 10^{-14}}{(2/9) \times 10^{-5}}\right\}*$$

$$= -(\overline{9}\cdot6352)$$

$$= -(-8\cdot3468)$$

i.e. the pH at which $0\cdot01M$ $AgNO_3$ begins to precipitate AgOH is approximately $8\cdot35$.

10. For solubility product values as small as $3\cdot5 \times 10^{-18}$, and in the absence of other electrolytes, the solubility product may be stated in terms of concentrations only. Hence,

$$[Hg_2^{++}][Cl^-]^2 = 3\cdot5 \times 10^{-18}$$

Let $[Hg_2^{++}] = x$, then for electrical neutrality

$$[Cl^-] = 2[Hg_2^{++}] = 2x$$

Hence, $$[Hg_2^{++}][Cl^-]^2 = x(2x)^2 = 4x^3 = 3\cdot5 \times 10^{-18}$$

Hence, $$x = \sqrt[3]{0\cdot875 \times 10^{-18}} = 0\cdot9567 \times 10^{-6}$$

i.e. the chloride ion concentration $(= 2x)$ is $1\cdot92 \times 10^{-6}$ moles per litre.

* In view of the approximation in the value of $(f_\pm) \simeq 0\cdot9$, no advantage is to be gained in using the exact value of K_w.

11. In a saturated solution of magnesium stearate (in equilibrium with the solid), we have

$$Mg(St)_2 = \underset{\text{Solid}}{} \quad Mg^{++} + 2St^-$$

Let $[Mg^{++}] = x = $ solubility, then $[St^-] = 2x$
Hence,

$$[Mg^{++}][St^-]^2 = x(2x)^2 = 4x^3 = \text{concentration solubility product}$$

But $[Mg^{++}] = \dfrac{\text{g of magnesium}}{\text{Molecular weight of Mg in g}} = \dfrac{3 \cdot 2 \times 100^{-3}\,\text{g}}{24 \cdot 32\,\text{g/mole}} = x$

Hence, the concentration solubility product is

$$4\left\{\frac{3 \cdot 2 \times 10^{-3}}{24 \cdot 32}\right\}^3 = 1 \cdot 457 \times 10^{-10}$$

Similarly, in a $0 \cdot 01\%$ NaCl solution, on putting $[Mg^{++}] = y$, we have $4y^3 = $ solubility product

$$= 4\left\{\frac{3 \cdot 84 \times 10^{-3}}{24 \cdot 32}\right\}^3 = 2 \cdot 519 \times 10^{-10}$$

12. For barium sulphate, $a_{Ba^{++}}\, a_{SO_4^-} = 10^{-10}$

$$a_{Ba^{++}} = \frac{10^{-10}}{a_{SO^-}} \qquad \qquad \text{(i)}$$

i.e. for barium sulphate to precipitate, equation (i) must be satisfied or, more precisely

$$a_{Ba^{++}} \geq \frac{10^{-10}}{a_{SO_4^-}} \qquad \qquad \text{(ia)}$$

For strontium sulphate to precipitate we have, similarly

$$a_{Sr^{++}} \geq \frac{3 \cdot 2 \times 10^{-7}}{a_{SO_4^-}} \qquad \qquad \text{(ii)}$$

Hence, the requirement for the precipitation of $BaSO_4$ is numerically smaller than that of $SrSO_4$. For a given $a_{SO_4^-}$, and dividing (ia) by (ii), we have

$$\frac{a_{Ba^{++}}}{a_{Sr^{++}}} > \frac{10^{-10}}{3 \cdot 2 \times 10^{-7}}$$

i.e. $> 3 \cdot 13 \times 10^{-4}$

that is, when the above ratio is below $3 \cdot 13 \times 10^{-4}$, precipitation of the strontium sulphate will begin to take place.

The answer to the second part of the problem is in the affirmative, because the activity coefficients of barium sulphate and strontium sulphate should be practically equal in such solutions and should therefore cancel.

13. $$I = \tfrac{1}{2}\Sigma m_i(z_i)^2$$

For Na_2SO_4: $0 \cdot 01 = \tfrac{1}{2}\{2m(1)^2 + m(2)^2\} = 3m$

Hence, $$m = \frac{0 \cdot 01}{3} = 3 \cdot 33 \times 10^{-3}$$

For $BaCl_2$: $\qquad 0 \cdot 01 = \tfrac{1}{2}\{m(2)^2 + 2m(1)^2\} = 3m$

$\therefore \qquad\qquad\qquad m = 3 \cdot 33 \times 10^{-3}$

For $ZnSO_4$: $\qquad 0 \cdot 01 = \tfrac{1}{2}\{m(2)^2 + m(2)^2\} = 4m$

$\therefore \qquad\qquad\qquad m = \dfrac{10^{-2}}{4} = 2 \cdot 5 \times 10^{-3}$

For NH_4Cl: $\qquad 0 \cdot 01 = \tfrac{1}{2}\{m(1)^2 + m(1)^2\} = m$

$\therefore \qquad\qquad\qquad m = 0 \cdot 01$

For $(NH_4)_2SO_4$: This electrolyte being uni-bivalent like Na_2SO_4, the molarity required is also $3 \cdot 33 \times 10^{-3}$

14. For NaCl: $\quad - \log f_{\pm} = 0 \cdot 5095 \sqrt{10^{-3}}$ (since I = molarity for uni-univalent electrolytes)

Hence, $$f_{\pm} = \text{antilog}\,(- 0 \cdot 5095 \sqrt{10^{-3}})$$
$$= \text{antilog}\,(- 0 \cdot 01611)$$
$$= \text{antilog}\,(\bar{1} \cdot 98389)$$
$$= 0 \cdot 9634$$

For $BaCl_2$: $\qquad I = 3 \times \text{molarity} = 3 \times 10^{-3}$

Hence, $\qquad - \log f_{\pm} = 1 \cdot 0 \sqrt{3 \times 10^{-3}}$

Hence, $\qquad \log f_{\pm} = - \sqrt{3 \times 10^{-3}}$

Therefore, $\qquad f_{\pm} = \text{antilog} - \sqrt{(3 \times 10^{-3})}$
$$= \text{antilog}\,(- 0 \cdot 05476)$$
$$= \text{antilog}\,(\bar{1} \cdot 94524)$$
$$= 0 \cdot 8814$$

For $La(NO_3)_3$: $\qquad I = \tfrac{1}{2}\{10^{-3}(3)^2 + 3 \times 10^{-3}(1)^2\} = 6 \times 10^{-3}$

Hence $\qquad - \log f_{\pm} = 1 \cdot 5 \sqrt{6 \times 10^{-3}}$

and $\qquad \log f_{\pm} = - (1 \cdot 5 \times \sqrt{6 \times 10^{-3}})$

Hence
$$f_{\pm} = \text{antilog} \left(- 1 \cdot 5 \times \sqrt{6 \times 10^{-3}} \right)$$
$$= \text{antilog} \left(- 0 \cdot 1162 \right)$$
$$= \text{antilog} \left(\bar{1} \cdot 8838 \right)$$
$$= 0 \cdot 7652$$

Experimentally, the value of $f_{\pm}$ for $0 \cdot 001 \text{M}$ $LaCl_3$ is $0 \cdot 853$. (It has already been pointed out that for high-valency electrolytes considerable divergences exist between the values of the activity coefficients as calculated using the Debye-Hückel equation and the corresponding ones determined experimentally.)

Author Index

(See pp. 100–2 for a list of references)

AKERLOF and Short, 27

BANCROFT, xv, 42
Bassett, 99
Belcher, 29
Bell, 99
Bjerrum, 28, 34, 99
Bockris, 99
Böttger, 34
Bradley, 98
Britton, 34, 98
Brønsted and LaMer, xvi, 74, 75
Bruner and Zawadsky, 35, 36, 89
Bunn, 57
Butler, 97

DEBYE and Hückel, xvi, 9, 10, 11, 74, 75
Denbigh, 97
Dundon and Mack, 57

ENGEL, 26

FEITKNECHT, 98
Forbes and Cole, 83
Fuoss, 99
    and Kraus, 28

GELOSO and Deschamps, 99
Glasstone, 34, 36, 54
Goates, Gordon and Faux, 89
Gurney, 99

HAMMARSTEN, 8
Hammett, 98
Harned and Owen, 99
Hildebrand, xv
Hullet and Duschak, 50, 57
Hume and Stone, 99

INGHAM, 23

JOHNSON and Adams, 51

KNAPP 57, 58
Kolthoff, 98

LAMER, xvi
Lange, 70
    and Robinson, 70
Latimer, 99
Lewin, 43, 98
Lewis and Randall, 9, 14, 59, 99

MAY and Kolthoff, 57, 58, 98
Milone and Ferrero, 57

NERNST, vii, xv, 2
Neumann, 8
Noyes, xv

OSTWALD, 28, 42, 98
    and Freundlich, 56
Owen, 78
    and Brinkley, 78

PARTINGTON, 97
Popoff and Neumann, 8

RANDALL and Lewis, 9, 14, 59, 99
Ravitz, 35, 98
Ringbom, 98
Robinson and Wallace, 70

SCHANOV, 28
Seidell, 26, 27, 77, 97
Smith, 62
Smits, 98
Sorensen, 86
Stieglitz, xvi

TAMMANN, 42, 98
Thiel and Gessner, 89

WASHBURN, 97
Whitby, 34

Subject Index

ACTIVITY, 84
  coefficient, 6, 7, 8, 9, 10, 65–9, 84–6, 112
  coefficient Tables, 68
  solid, 6, 54–8, 73
  water, 71, 72
Adsorption, 50, 56
Ageing, 98
Avogadro number, 80

BASIC salts, 19, 20, 21, 98, 99

COLLOID formation, 48
Common ion effect, 12
Complex ions, 28–32, 99

DEHYDRATION, 22–7, 82
Dielectric constant, 56–8
Dipole, 4
  moment, 62–4
  water, 4, 5, 35
Distribution coefficient, 17

EQUILIBRIUM, attainment of, 5
  constant, 2–8, 37–40, 53, 58, 70, 89
  lack of, conditions, 41–6

FREE energy, 20, 55

GELS, 42, 49

HEAT of reaction, 37, 38, 78, 109
Hydration, 3–5, 66, 84, 99
Hydrogen sulphide, 85, 89, 91

IONIC product, 38, 39, 43, 44
  of water, 38–39, 93
Ionic strength, 6, 8, 9, 11, 38–9, 59–61, 90, 108, 113
Ionization—
  partial, 33–6, 83, 84
  degree of, 33, 34

KINETIC considerations, 81

MEDIUM, change of, 22–7
Metastable forms, vii, 49
Molecular velocities, 81

NICKEL ammines, 30, 31
Non-stable conditions, 47–51

pH, 93, 94, 110
Precipitation—
  of AgCl, 12, 14, 15, 81, 107
  of AgBr, 16–19, 103, 109
  of AgI 16–19
  of Ag(OH), 109, 110
  of Ag$_2$CrO$_4$, 106, 107, 109
  of BaCO$_3$, 107, 108
  of BaSO$_4$, 8, 43, 45, 106–8, 111
  of CdS, 29, 36
  of CuSO$_4$, 26
  of Group III metals, 30
  of HgS, 80, 81
  of Hg$_2$Cl$_2$, 110
  of KCl, 27
  of Mg(OH)$_2$, 92, 93
  of NaCl, 23, 24, 27, 82
  of NiS, 45
  of ZnS, viii, 45, 46, 84
  rapid under equilibrium conditions, vii, 13, 14

SILVER ammine 104, 105, 106
Solid solutions, 16–19
Solubility product—
  comprehensive, 4, 52–3, 70–5
  reduced, 2, 3
  thermodynamic derivation, 52–3
  values, 76–8
Surface tension, 56, 57, 58

THERMODYNAMIC considerations, 47, 49, 52, 53

WATER dipole association with ions, 5, 21, 24, 35
Water molecule dipole moment, 4, 5, 35